PATENTS AND PROGRESS

Patents and Progress

The Sources and Impact of Advancing Technology

58

Edited by

WROE ALDERSON
Late Professor of Marketing

VERN TERPSTRA
Assistant Professor of Marketing

Wharton School of Finance and Commerce, University of Pennsylvania

STANLEY J. SHAPIRO
Director, Marketing Planning
Canadian Advertising Agency, Ltd., Montreal

1965 • RICHARD D. IRWIN, INC. • HOMEWOOD, ILLINOIS

First Printing, September, 1965

Library of Congress Catalog Card No. 65–27837

PRINTED IN THE UNITED STATES OF AMERICA

To E. J. Carroll

In friendly recognition of a common
interest in the dynamics of competition.

FOREWORD

This volume is the first in a series designed to deal with various aspects of modern competition. The series as a whole is directed to the business economist and the marketing economist as well as to the general economist. In fact, the series grew out of a conversation between the senior editor and one of the most respected business economists in the Philadelphia region. We have taken the liberty of dedicating this volume to him as an individual even though his company has said that it does not wish to take any special credit for this venture in economic education.

The generous grant which has been provided has enabled us to schedule special lectures at the University of Pennsylvania by some of the most distinguished economists and social scientists in the United States. This volume contains all of the lectures presented during 1964.

The special subject of this first volume is technological change. The contributors approach the subject from various perspectives. The essays in Part 1 are largely concerned with the sources of technological change; the forces which produce it; the industrial climate which favors it; and the special incentives which encourage the inventor and the innovator. The essays in Part 2 emphasize the impact of technological change on the nature of competition and on public policy with respect to competition. The areas of public policy which are affected by the acceleration of technological change include policy in granting patents, policy with respect to government support or participation in projects resulting in patentable ideas, anti-trust policy, and policies of the Federal government designed to foster or favor small business enterprise.

The Patent Office is one of the oldest and most honored bureaus in the Federal government. It is undergoing severe strains at the present time because of the increasing magnitude and complexity of its task. It now has a backlog of three and a half years in unprocessed cases. The backlog could quickly grow to double that size unless some remedy is found for the administrative problems of the Patent Office. Increased salaries and career expectations for patent examiners could help since many of the best examiners leave after a few years to engage in the practice of patent law. Some who are close to the Patent Office are convinced that computerized patent search could make a major contribution to the reduction of the backlog but admit that several years must elapse before appropriate computers could be installed and programmed for this enormous task of storage and retrieval.

Some of the greatest difficulties of the patent system are beyond the jurisdiction of the Patent Office. Patent litigation and its abuses give color to the claim that patents in the hands of a large company enable it to exert monopoly power. The mere threat of legal action is enough to warn weaker firms off. The plaintiff has unlimited right to sue so long as he sues in different jurisdictions or can find a new cause of action after one claim has been disallowed. There are circuit courts in which practically no patent has been sustained and others in which almost no patent has ever been held invalid.

The need for an international patent system embracing all countries has long been recognized. The United States government has been working to achieve that end. While there is an international agreement to which many nations subscribe, there are some notable exceptions. One of these is Soviet Russia. There is a real chance that Russia may wish to join in the near future since it is increasingly confronted with the need to protect its own inventions.

The entry of the Federal government as a positive factor in technological advance through its sponsorship of research and development programs has created thorny issues. Where all or most of the money comes from government, should the patentable ideas which result belong to the government? Those who think they should not have argued that government is not well qualified for the private exploitation of technical ideas. They cite the fact that very little ever came of the efforts of the Alien Property Custodian to license the German patents confiscated during the war. Some of these patents were very valuable but few companies displayed any interest since the government proposed to license them to any other applicant rather than extending patent protection to the first suitable licensee.

The Sherman anti-trust statute was enacted largely because of public concern over the concentration of patents held by individual companies or patent pools. One of the targets of the trust-busting era was the patents held in trust for firms which participated in these great combinations. Anti-trust laws have been revised and extended since that time, and the acceleration of technological advance has placed patents in a rather different light in relation to monopoly and the problems of maintaining competition.

The treatment of anti-trust policy in this volume is not confined to the monopoly dangers arising from patents. There is evidence in some of the papers that anti-trust enforcement is developing a backlog which far exceeds the backlog of the Patent Office. That is to say, there is an increasing gap between the task of enforcement as conceived by the Department of Justice and the Federal Trade Commission and what they have been able to accomplish in their joint efforts in curbing tendencies toward monopoly and maintaining the vigor of competition. There is even a greater gap developing between the whole conception of anti-trust policy and the realities of the market place which the enforcement agencies are attempting to regulate.

Having testified in several leading anti-trust cases over the last twenty years, the senior editor has been puzzled by several features of these cases, including the almost whimsical way in which cases are selected for prosecution out of the many possibilities which must be available. In the first case, under Section 7 of the Clayton Act as revised, Pillsbury was charged with contributing to a monopoly trend even though it had only 9 percent of the flour market after acquiring Ballard & Ballard of Louisville. An offsetting consideration was that this acquisition for the first time presented General Mills with a truly national competitor.

In the 1958 request of the meat packers for relief from the consent decree, one could not help but wonder why the Department of Justice itself had not initiated action to moderate or rescind the consent decree in the interest of maintaining competition. These lumbering dinosaurs, the meat packers who originally accepted the consent decree, had long ago ceased to be effective competitors, partly because they were expressly forbidden to engage in any innovation in a long list of product fields which might otherwise appear attractive. The consent decree was entered into in 1920 and one of the strongest reasons cited was that the competition of the meat packers would put wholesale grocers out of business. Yet in 1958, when the packers made their last unsuccessful plea for relief, the largest wholesale branch of a meat packer would have fitted neatly on the loading dock of a large wholesale grocery operation.

Public policy should be as much concerned about nourishing small business as about policing big business. Efforts to aid small business have largely concentrated on its financial problems. A generation ago the Department of Commerce made a promising start toward providing analytical services and demonstration projects for small business paralleling on a much more modest scale what had been done for the farmer through the county agent system. Perhaps some special assistance in the area of patents should be considered, such as extending the period of patent protection for a small company organized to promote a specific patent.

Returning to the factors favoring the advance of technology discussed in Part 1, it would appear that providing adequate incentives for disclosure is still fundamental in promoting technical advance as visualized by the authors of the United States Constitution. The shift from the individual inventor to the salaried engineer producing patentable ideas for his employer has been almost complete in some of the more advanced industries. Where this has happened there can be no doubt that deliberate invention and innovation have come to be a vital part of the whole economic process. In fact, there has been an increasing tendency for marketing research to precede technical research or to be carried out in coordination with it. For the market analyst, devoting a large part of his attention to the problem of introducing new products, it seems strange that the process of innovation should have ever been regarded as lying outside the realm of economic calculation of costs and benefits.

It has been proposed that the hired inventor should have all the rights of the independent inventor, including that of receiving royalties from his employer on his invention. This proposition apparently does not recognize the basic shift which has taken place in the available incentives and their appeal. The true independent was often a man with a passion who was willing to live on a restricted scale for the sake of a dream. His dream of wealth was like that of the man who buys tickets on the Irish sweepstakes. The trained design engineer who agrees to assign to his employer any patents arising from his work has elected the safer course of a comfortable and continuing income. It is difficult to see why he should have it both ways as a matter of right, shifting the risk to his employer but collecting royalties if he should come up with a profitable invention, the employer having also provided a laboratory and technical assistants.

The problem of public policy is how best to stimulate invention and how to bring the fruits of invention to market. The inventor is only one of the essential elements in the total process of innovation and market entry. If he chooses to work alone and has the spark of genius, he will sometimes come up with a more fundamental advance than is likely to result from a company program of research and development. Thereafter, he will have the problems of organizing a company or otherwise disposing of his patent which requires quite a different set of skills.

The use of hired inventors surely represents a less wasteful use of inventive talent. The inventor can invent while working in a company environment, which assures specialized support in other areas such as finance and marketing. Both types of arrangement are needed to fulfill the promise of continuing economic growth. Public policy intervenes further in supporting research where it seems desirable to accelerate invention and innovation. Any of these arrangements whereby invention takes place, whether through the independent inventor, the hired inventor, the university researcher, or the government sponsored research project, must eventually meet the test of the market. The prospects of success must offer a reasonable expectation of returns in relation to the costs. The marketing technician comes into the picture after the invention has been made and, on the average, undertakes the more difficult part of the task to judge by the large majority of inventions which never gain a foothold in the market.

The market analyst has never been able to ignore the advances in marketing technology because it has been his business to help produce them. These marketing advances are often quite as impressive as the improvements in products or production techniques. Some regard it as a paradox that marketing improvements are occurring at an accelerated rate despite the fact that there is no patent protection available in marketing. There are several reasons why this happens, only one of which need be mentioned here. Marketing innovations are internal to the process of moving goods to market and are a direct expression of market competition. The advantages of operating at or near capacity in mass production and mass distribution make the pressures for marketing innovation irresistible. Even though these advantages may be quickly eroded away, the aggressive competitor hopes to maintain his lead by pioneering further improvements in marketing.

A dynamic view of competition emerges naturally from a book concerned with technological change. Modern competition is largely concerned with deliberate efforts to improve products and to improve the methods of marketing them. Passive adaptation in the market place has given way to a systematic and continuous drive to solve problems. Competition among problem-solvers is inherently dynamic.

Aside from the authors who have contributed to this volume, we are indebted to the chairmen who presided over the several sessions and who were able to stimulate a lively and useful discussion from the floor. These chairmen included Dr. Fritz Macklup, a leading authority on patents and technological change; Dr. Louis B. Schwartz, Professor of Law and university professor at the University of Pennsylvania; and Dr. Willis J. Winn, Dean of the Wharton School of Commerce and Finance.

WROE ALDERSON
VERN TERPSTRA
STANLEY J. SHAPIRO

May, 1965

TABLE OF CONTENTS

PART 1
THE SOURCES OF
TECHNOLOGICAL CHANGE

In searching for sources of technological change, Schmookler addresses himself to the question of whether inventive activity is an exogenous variable (like the weather) or an endogenous variable in the analysis of industrial growth. After study of data on patents issued in the United States, and consideration of 900 major inventions made all over the world, he concludes that invention is generally an economic activity—it responds to economic pressures and incentives, quite unlike the rain. Thus he finds that the rate of technical change in an industry depends more on the industry's rate of growth than vice versa, and that investment leads inventive activity rather than following it.

JACOB SCHMOOKLER is Professor of Economics at the University of Minnesota. He received his A.B. degree from Temple and has an M.A. and Ph.D. degree from the University of Pennsylvania. He has published such articles as "Changing Efficiency of the American Economy 1869–1938," *Review of Economics and Statistics;* "Changes in Industry and in the State of Knowledge as Determinants of Inventive Activity"; and "Economic Sources of Inventive Activity," appearing in the *Journal of Economic History.*

CHAPTER 1

TECHNOLOGICAL CHANGE
AND THE
LAW OF INDUSTRIAL GROWTH*

Jacob Schmookler

While neoclassical economic theory has many important applications, it is only poorly related to what really happens in the long run. It suffers from this deficiency mainly because it makes no provision for changes in technological knowledge. Such changes obviously can be taken into account by shifts of the supply curve. Indeed, this is a major use of comparative statics. Yet this is precisely the trouble—technological change has to be introduced into the analysis from the outside. It is therefore assumed, not explained. Thus, what is certainly one of the most important determinants of price and output in the long run is entirely outside the range of the theory.

Of course it can be argued, that whether or not economists should account for technological change itself, as distinct from its economic effects, depends on whether technological change is itself substantially influenced by economic variables. To take an analogous case, to explain the price of wheat we may need to know the amount of rainfall. Yet under present circumstances one may defensibly contend that it is not an economist's business to *explain* the amount of rainfall.

---

* The author's research mentioned below is described more extensively in his "Changes in Industry and in the State of Knowledge as Determinants of Industrial Invention" in Richard R. Nelson (ed.), *The Rate and Direction of Inventive Activity: Economic and Social Factors* (Princeton: 1962); "Economic Sources of Inventive Activity," *Journal of Economic History*, XXII (March 1962); his joint paper with O. H. Brownlee, "Determinants of Inventive Activity," *American Economic Review, Proceedings*, May 1962; and his joint communication with Zvi Griliches, "Inventing and Maximizing," same journal, September, 1963.

We simply take it as given. This position is logical and often necessary in the short run but it is also seldom satisfactory in the long run. It may be necessary in the short run because economists are not meteorologists. It may be unsatisfactory in the long run because an inability to predict rainfall may subject our predictions of the price of wheat to unacceptable ranges of error. Hence, if the matter is sufficiently pressing the best way to advance the science of economics in the long run may be to advance the science of meteorology. Whether this means that meteorology should be advanced by economists or by others is an open question. It is relevant, however, to record that the recent notable advances in understanding of biological phenomena have come from physics, and have led to the development of a whole new and exciting field—molecular biology. The history of science is replete with comparable instances of fusion, although fission seems more common. In general, while the domain of any science seems to be dominated in the short run by its inherited techniques, intellectual and physical, in the long run it seems to be dominated by its underlying subject matter. It is a fair guess that future biologists will be better-trained in physics than are their present-day counterparts. And it would not be surprising if agricultural economists learned more than the rest of us about meteorology, even if they make no contributions to it.

What really complicates the issue is not the question of proper strategy in drawing useful boundaries for the economics profession. The real problem will arise when rainfall is converted from an act of nature into an industry. Once that happens, the price of wheat may be one of the indices used in deciding how much rain we want. If that day comes, regardless of their range of error, pre-existing predictive models for the price of wheat will no longer be satisfactory, for the price of wheat will then help determine rainfall which will as before, help determine supply, which helps determine the price of wheat. What was an exogenous variable determined outside the model will become a partially endogenous one determined partly inside it. Willy-nilly, economists will become predictors of the output of rain without becoming meteorologists, as they are predictors of farmers' planting intentions without being agronomists.

Now the question I would like to consider is whether technological change, defined as additions to the social stock of industrially useful knowledge, is in the same class of phenomena as the weather until now, influencing economic activity but not influenced by it. Or whether it is like the weather of the hypothetical future just described, both influencing and influenced by economic activity. I am concerned, in short, with the question of whether in the large view of things, technological change is an exogenous variable or endogenous one.

Now, I think it is obvious that the answer to this question cannot be all black or all white. Some technological change is accidental, and some of it clearly originates from the efforts of pure scientists—men whose only goal is understanding, but who produce useful knowledge as an unsought by-product. To the extent that it reflects such factors, technological change is clearly exogenous for most purposes. Moreover, it is entirely possible, if not indeed likely, that the relative importance of exogenous technological change has changed over time. Hence, to be more precise, I am concerned with the question of whether technological change has been *primarily* one or the other over the last century or two.

There is an even deeper aspect of this question which I must at least allude to here. A given phenomenon may be exogenous in some of its dimensions and endogenous in others. Hence, let me further limit the topic by saying that because my own research bears directly only on this phenomenon, that my immediate concern is with the allocation of the amount of inventing among different end-uses—e.g., the distribution of inventive activity at a given point in time among capital goods for different industries; and with variations over time in the amount of inventive activity devoted to a given end-use. Later, in the course of my paper, I will broaden the topic somewhat.

Much light on these questions is shed by two bodies of data. One consists of over a fifth of all the United States patents ever issued, reclassified on the basis of industry of use. These data cover the period 1837–1957 on an annual basis. For the period 1874–1950 the patents are counted as of the date of application; for other years, as of the date of grant. The patent data have undoubted defects—those resulting from my own deficiencies is well as those which are inherent in them. But they are the most comprehensive available, the items which comprise them have all passed a rather rigorous examination for novelty administered in accord with what would appear to be a rather stable set of criteria, and they yield interesting results.

The second class of data consists of descriptions of over 900 important inventions made anywhere in the world since 1800 in paper making, petroleum refining, farming, and railroading. While these inventions were painstakingly selected from an enormous literature by competent researchers, temporal variations in the proportion of important inventions included are almost certainly considerable.

The behavior of these two classes of data throws much light on the issue of whether inventive activity and, by implication, technological change are or are not independent of economic activity. One theme in modern thought that recurs so often, that is built into the very phraseology of the language and indeed is one of the great organizing principles of social thought, is the idea that inventions—at least modern inventions—spring from scientific discovery. This conception of events is reflected, for example, in the very expression, research and development, and it is embodied in the common belief that the course of modern history has somehow been shaped by scientific discoveries.

With this hypothesis in mind we were extremely interested in finding out the nature of the events or conditions which stimulated inventors to create the 900-plus important inventions in the four industries mentioned above. The literature unfortunately was silent in most cases, but on several hundred cases the record was clear. Sometimes the initiating stimulus was an accident. Usually, however, it was an event or condition conceived by the inventor in economic terms—a felt deficiency in the product or process of one sort or other. In only two or three cases did there seem a bona fide possibility that a scientific discovery provided the immediate stimulus to the making of the invention. The most probable of these perhaps was V. N. Ipatieff's work on hydrogenation of petroleum which came a few years after Paul A. Sabatier's Nobel prize-winning work on hydrogenation.

Of course, many of these important inventions were *possible* only because certain scientific discoveries preceded them. (Many others, however, owed to science at most a spirit of inquiry and an empirical attitude toward phenomena.) But it seems probable from our analysis—and I think the same conclusion applies to the major twentieth-century inventions turned up by Jewkes, Sawers, and

Stillerman—that major inventions are made normally because particular economic problems have become more pressing or economic opportunities have become more inviting, and not because some scientific finding suddenly pushed them over the horizon.

We also tried to check the commonly held related idea that inventive activity in a field generally flows as major inventions create new possibilities and ebbs when major inventions decline. Again, the question is not whether these major inventions are necessary for the minor ones which imitate, modify, adapt, and supplement them. That this is so goes without saying. What we were interested in rather is the validity of the proposition that inventive activity in a field is primarily a routine, direct response to the major inventions in that field. Let me first note that inventive activity in any pair of competing fields—say, metal buildings and wooden buildings, or leather nailing and leather sewing—tends to be synchronized over the short run. This short-run synchronization of competitive fields obviously suggests that common external forces dominate their course.

Second, it is noteworthy that major inventions on the whole fluctuate with inventive activity in their fields. This being so, they can hardly be classed as prime determinants of invention in their fields. There are some interesting qualifications to this conclusion, the most important being that the major inventions which create a field seem to be a relatively larger component of total inventive activity in that field at the outset. Even this may be an optical illusion resulting from the natural bias of the chroniclers of the growth of an industry's technology toward recording industry-establishing inventions while ignoring inventions of equal economic magnitude which came later.

Keynes once suggested that the current economic cant of a politician usually represents the doctrine of some academician of an earlier day. By this example he sought to demonstrate the power of ideas. His example was telling as far as it went, but it did not go as far as he thought. What he showed was that ideas tend to live on beyond the period of their usefulness, in the minds of laymen and scientists alike. What he neglected to note, and what his own works so vividly illustrate, is that it is this very loss of utility which stimulates active and independent minds to discard inherited notions and invent new ones. In the end it is experience which rules.

In short, Keynes' remark was addressed to the transmission and persistence of ideas. The influence of ideas considered from this vantage point is indeed great. On the other hand, if we ask why ideas *arise*, then at least in the technological realm and very possibly in other realms as well, they are triggered ordinarily not by the mere birth of antecedent ideas but by life itself. And one may add, it is experience, too, which accounts not only for the birth but also for the death of ideas, although, admittedly, some ideas die hard.

Let me repeat, however, I am not trying to say that scientific discovery is without influence on inventive activity. Certainly for well-educated inventors (it is surprising how many are not), received science sets the conceptual framework in one dimension, and such men undoubtedly file news of new, interesting discoveries for future reference. Moreover, whole fields, like chemistry and electricity, owe their start to scientific discoveries. It is important, however, to recognize that fields such as these, unlike food, clothing, shelter, etc., are essentially not consumer goods fields—though they occasionally produce substitutes for older consumer products. Chemistry, electricity and analogous fields are largely intermediate goods in the realm of knowledge classified economically, and I suspect that the intensity with which they are cultivated at any given time is proportional to their prospective contributions, insofar as these can be anticipated, toward the satisfaction of private and public wants.

The foregoing brings me to the positive side of our findings. Broadly speaking, our results indicate that inventive activity in a field tends very much to fluctuate along with economic activity in that field.

Originally it appeared that total inventive activity in the United States varied directly with economy-wide employment of labor and capital combined. This result supported the hypotheses that the potential saving in total cost constituted the source of prospective profit from inventing, that such potential saving would tend to be proportional to total cost of production, and that therefore inventive activity would tend to vary with the total cost, i.e., the volume of resources employed.[1] This chain of reasoning later proved mistaken. Measures of the two were indeed highly correlated but they were

---

[1] Cf. the author's "The Level of Inventive Activity," *Review of Economics and Statistics*, May, 1954.

equally correlated with a third variable—gross investment, and this now appears to have been the critical one.

This error was revealed once the statistics of patents classified by industry were available and patents in the railroad field were compared with an index of total input in the railroad industry. No similarity emerged such as that which had appeared earlier in the case of aggregate inventive activity and total national input. Instead we found that railroad investment and railroad patents were very similar in their long-run and shorter-run movements. The main difference between them, and a very suggestive difference it was, was that the patent statistics lagged slightly behind those of investment.

A similar moving average of railroad stock prices, adjusted for changes in the general level of wholesale prices, was also substantially synchronized with investment and invention, with stock prices tending to lead the other two. These general relationships definitely hold in the long run, with railroad stock prices and railroad patents rising to all-time peaks in 1908 and investment in 1911. The relations hold with comparable clarity over Kuznets cycles—cycles of about 15 to 20 years in duration. On a year-to-year basis they are not so evident.

Since this initial discovery we have checked for the existence of a similar relation between investment and invention in capital goods fields in a wide variety of industries. Wherever the economic data existed to compare with the capital goods patent series, that relation has been found. That is, the ebb and flow of investment, or something associated with it, seems to induce a corresponding ebb and flow of inventive activity directed toward improving the capital goods.

Moreover, when we shifted from intertemporal comparisons within an industry to cross-section comparisons involving several industries at the same time, the same relation was observed. Just as more inventive activity is devoted to improving an industry's equipment when more of that equipment is being produced, so more inventive activity is devoted toward improving capital goods in those industries which are buying more equipment. For example, when 1939 investment per worker is correlated with capital goods patents per worker in 1940–42, the simple coefficient of determination, r^2, is about .6.

Finally, it was possible to compare the course of output of railroad freight cars, passenger cars, locomotives and rails with patents in each of those fields from about 1860 or 1870 to about 1950. In every case the respective long term patterns and major cycles were similar, and in some instances even the year-to-year movements were remarkably alike.

I think it is fair to say that these results are the complete reverse of a priori expectations, for most of us would have expected investment to follow inventive activity, not lead it. These common expectations are traceable to a long, honored, and active tradition going back even beyond Schumpeter's *Theory of Economic Development* and forward even more recently than Salter's *Productivity and Technical Progress*. The most recent development along this line consists of correlations between rates of industrial growth and R & D expenditures as a percent of sales, with the obvious and, I think, erroneous inference commonly drawn that the observed high positive correlation between the two variables implies that industries grow faster than others because they do relatively more R & D. The fundamental interpretation of such correlations, I think, is simply that R & D is more profitable in industries with a greater growth potential, and that the ranking of industries with respect to growth rates over the last few decades would not have been much different if there had been no technological progress whatever—although the growth rates of some would have been lower and others higher.

In other words, while invention does affect investment and the rate of growth of an industry, and may affect them deeply, such effects are not the only important feature of the connection between invention on the one hand and investment and growth on the other. This must be true, given the timing relations among the variables disclosed in the research I have summarized above.

The significant question is implied by the fact that inventive activity in a capital goods field tends to vary directly with the output of the capital goods concerned. I think the best guess is that invention in a field is likely to be more profitable when the class of goods it pertains to is selling, or is expected to sell, well; and that when invention is more profitable more of it is done. The implication of this for the underlying question of this paper is obvious. Whatever it may legitimately be in the framework of some other discipline, from the standpoint of economics invention is mainly an economic activity. As in other economic activities, resources tend to be allocated among its branches, and probably between it and other classes of economic activity, in accord with profit expectations.

Probably there are also other factors, likewise economic in nature, that contribute to the empirical results observed. Specifically, the funds available for support of inventive activity in a given field, the manpower available to carry it out, and the amount of attention focused on the field are all likely to be positively associated with the amount of economic activity in the field itself. But the dominant influence on the amount of inventing in a field seems to be the income expected from it.

Against this background let us turn next to the Law of Industrial Growth. The law is essentially a generalization, based on observation, which holds that the trend curve of output of any industry, when plotted on an arithmetic scale, tends to inscribe an S-shaped pattern. The percentage rate of growth generally declines with time. I would like to examine the adequacy of the dominant current explanation for this characteristic pattern, in particular, the role which technological change is assumed to play in causing it.

A completely satisfactory explanation of the growth curve must account for the birth of the industry, the subsequent retardation in the annual percentage rate of growth of output, the maximum trend value of the output, and its subsequent decline if any. As I have no particular fault to find with contemporary explanations of declining industries I shall confine my discussion to the creation, rate of growth, and maximum value.

Generally speaking, I think it is fair to say that the circumstances leading to the birth of a new industry have received little attention in discussions of the law. The discussions have tended to commence their account after the industry has already been created. Insofar as the birth of the industry is considered it all, the authors are content to allude to the major inventions and their scientific antecedents, if any, which made the industry technically possible. Thus, the emphasis is implicitly entirely on the readiness of the state of knowledge for the making of the basic inventions at the time, or on the self-assignment of inventors to the task of creating the industry's technology.[2]

---

[2] Cf. Simon Kuznets, *Secular Movements in Production and Prices* (Boston, 1930), Chap. 1; or W. E. G. Salter, *Productivity and Technical Change* (New York: Cambridge University Press, 1960), p. 133.

Any such explanation is in principle unsatisfactory, for it rests on the untenable premise that what can happen will. To assert that an invention is made because it was possible to make it, or that a commodity will be produced because it has been invented is on a par with the statement that the Golden Gate Bridge was built because the building art permitted it.

The missing ingredient, of course, is the anticipated demand for the product. Inventions are made not only because they are possible but also because they are thought to be desirable. It is indeed a curious fact that while economists have insisted on the paramountcy of demand in determining the allocation of productive resources in analyzing the static case, they tend utterly to abandon this frame of reference in analyzing the S-shaped growth curve. And it is perhaps no less curious that while economic historians as a class have been among the leading critics of static economic theory, in dealing with dynamics industrial and technological historians have tended to assign to demand a far more active role than economists have.[3]

Our research indicates that important inventions in established industries are generally made because some problem has become more urgent or some opportunity more appealing. Whether this would prove to be likewise the case with basic, industry-establishing inventions is a question which only further research can answer. Undoubtedly, such research would reveal instances in which the underlying demand existed for a long time and only the requisite knowledge had to be developed to tap it; and other instances would appear in which the requisite knowledge existed for a long time but the anticipated demand was too slight to make invention seem worthwhile. Moreover, we should not be surprised to find still other instances in which all that was missing for a long time was a man who recognized that the demand and the knowledge required to meet it were both there.

But in any event, whatever results would be secured from such an investigation of industry-generating inventions, demand would have to be assigned an integral role in their explanation, for the only

---

[3] Cf. Thomas Beer, *The Emergence of the German Dye Industry* (Urbana: University of Illinois Press, 1959); H. F. Williamson and A. R. Daum, *The American Petroleum Industry*, (Evanston, Ill.: Northwestern University Press, 1959), Vol. I; Christopher E. Savage, *An Economic History of Transport* (London: Hillary House Publishers, 1959); and Carl W. Condit, *American Building Art: The Nineteenth Century* (New York: Oxford University Press, 1960).

genuine issue is not whether the potential demand existed but how long it existed before the knowledge required to satisfy it was created.

If the traditional view does not say enough to explain the birth of new industries, perhaps it says too much in explaining the pattern of growth of established industries. For in dealing with the characteristic long-term retardation in the percentage rate of growth, the traditional explanation not only includes factors which properly belong, but it indeed places its *primary* reliance upon a factor of doubtful significance. The current view, appropriately, recognizes the possible influence of both demand and supply—the influence of demand being exhibited in price—and income-elasticities, and in demand shifts caused by population changes and by the development of rival products or of rival foreign industries; and the influence of supply being revealed in the pressure of resource increments in the given industry upon alternative uses for the same resources, and perhaps in supply shifts occasioned by the discovery or depletion of irreproducible natural resources.

While factors such as those just enumerated very properly belong in any discussion of factors affecting the growth of an industry, they do not necessarily add up to retardation in the rate of growth.

Businessmen and students of marketing would, I suspect, account for the retardation phenomenon very simply and, I believe, adequately, in terms of an asymptotic approach to market saturation. There is, after all, a limit to the number of TV sets, lawn mowers, or aspirin tablets any population will want under the most favorable circumstances, and circumstances are seldom wholly favorable for any given industry. Given an upper limit to the potential market, the industry will tend to become less profitable as the limit is approached. Hence, entry of new firms and expansion of old ones will slow down, and output will grow at a declining rate.

Just why economists have chosen to ignore or at least deemphasize this very obvious possibility in accounting for the Law of Industrial Growth is not clear. In any event they have in fact placed their primary reliance instead on the questionable assumption that as an industry ages and more inventions are made in it, the opportunities for further invention decline. The rate of technical progress, it is claimed, tends to slacken. This in turn leads to a slowing down in the rate of fall of prices and therefore, presumably, in the rate of growth of output. (The emphasis in the literature in these discussions is on cost-cutting rather than product-improving inventions. I shall follow suit, but the analysis could, I think, be generalized.)

I suspect that the rate of technical progress in an industry usually does slow down as the industry grows older, although the recent rapid technical progress in such old industries as farming and soft coal mining suggests that if the rule holds generally, there may be important exceptions to it. But even if technical progress falls off, we are still left with the problem of explaining why it does. According to the traditional view, the basic industry-establishing inventions constitute, so to speak, a fixed factor. The application of successive doses of inventive effort is then subject to the law of diminishing marginal returns, returns being measured, say, in terms of percentage cuts in cost per unit of output. The rate at which diminishing returns to inventive effort occurs is then held to determine the industry's rate of growth of output.

Is this really the case? In the first place, while it is reasonable to suppose that the inventive potential in some fields exceeds that in others at a moment of time, and that the relative potentials in different fields change over time, there is absolutely no evidence that the potential within any reasonably complex field declines as the field advances. Nor is there any basis for supposing that anything approaching the potential is ever realized. To argue that the ultimate decline of invention in any given field proves that the field's inventive potential has declined is no more logical than the argument that the decline in the output of bows and arrows proves that their potential output has declined.

In the second place, we know that capital-output ratios tend to decline within individual industries over time. Hence if, as suggested above, the rate of growth of output declines because the market is approaching saturation, capital formation in the industry will tend to decline absolutely while output is still rising. Then, given that invention in a capital goods field tends to follow the course of capital goods output, invention and therefore presumably the rate of technological progress would likewise decline. Since each new unit of capital will exhibit a smaller improvement than formerly while the average age of capital will rise, the measured rate of technical progress will tend to decline. The same reasoning would, I think, apply to technological progress that is not embodied in new capital goods.

What I am saying, in short, is that the conventional explanation of the Law of Industrial Growth largely reverses cause and effect. The decline in the rate of technical progress is not the chief cause of the decline in the rate of growth of an industry, although it undoubtedly contributes toward that result. Rather, the decline in the rate of growth of the industry causes its rate of technical progress to slow down. The main reason for the retardation in the rate of growth is, in all likelihood, the limited demand for the product.

The hypothesis that the rate of technical change depends on the rate of growth receives direct support from economic and engineering studies of individual enterprises. These studies have found that cost per unit of output varies inversely with the number of units of the good ever produced by the firm. Studies of such diverse items as machine tools, airframes, radar sets, etc., indicate that a doubling of the cumulative output generates a cut in unit costs of about twenty percent.[4] This result, according to the researchers who have found it, is to be explained by the improved methods which come from experience. The results imply that a constant percentage rate of growth of output per year will result in a constant percentage rate of technical progress, and that a decline in the rate of growth of output will bring with it a decrease in the rate of technical progress. Whether substantially the same relationship will be found to prevail for an entire industry in the long run remains to be demonstrated. As they stand, however, these results are very consistent with the hypothesis that the rate of technical progress depends more on the rate of growth than vice versa.

In sum, new consumer goods and cost-cutting methods tend to be invented when inventing them promises to be profitable. The evidence suggests that in modern societies inventions tend to arise when the demand for them is strong enough. However, the premise that inventive activity is a particular form of economic activity does not rest on this evidence. Purposeful invention is economic by its very nature, for to identify a direction of inquiry as one which may lead to

---

[4] Cf. L. E. Preston and E. C. Keachie, "Cost Functions and Progress Functions," *American Economic Review*, March, 1964, and the references at the end of their communication.

an invention is simply to suggest a better way of satisfying a want. Since market-oriented want-satisfying activity is economic activity, inventive activity is one kind of economic activity.

Moreover, if, as seems only reasonable to suppose, inventors tend to choose that one among alternative lines of inquiry which promises the greatest economic success, then inventors behave as economic agents are generally presumed to behave. This is true whether they typically first sense a need and then search for the most promising means of meeting it as the research reported above suggests, or first learn a new scientific theory and then search for the most profitable field in which to apply it as many feel is the case.

Hence, it seems reasonable to assume that the demand for a product is a major determinant of the returns which can be expected from inventing improvements in it. If this is correct, neoclassical economic theory is deficient because it encompasses only routine economic behavior. It is perhaps this attribute of the theory which unwittingly led economists interested in explaining dynamic phenomena such as the S-shaped growth curve to treat technological progress as primarily noneconomic in origin. In consequence, they created the paradox that while the consumer was king in the hypothetical static world of neoclassical theory, he was only a lowly pawn in the dynamic economy of the real world. If the argument advanced here is correct, he is sovereign in both worlds.

Social Scientist Pool considers recent significant changes in the social environment of science and asks, "What is the proper social environment and reward system for sustained technological growth?" He finds the educational process ("the two-decade development cycle") to be a critical factor in the supply of creativity for today's—and tomorrow's—world of rapid technical change. He suggests that the more creative scientists are quite interested in money as a reward, but that if we can innovate to order, perhaps the reward should be for the focus of the innovation rather than for the fact of innovation.

ITHIEL de SOLA POOL is Professor of political science and director of the International Communications Program of the Center for International Studies at Massachusetts Institute of Technology. He is also a fellow of the American Academy of Arts and Sciences and the American Association for the Advancement of Science. He received his B.A., M.A., and Ph.D. degrees from the University of Chicago. He is author of *American Business and Public Policy: The Politics of Foreign Trade.*

CHAPTER 2

THE SOCIAL ENVIRONMENT
FOR SUSTAINED
TECHNOLOGICAL GROWTH

Ithiel de Sola Pool

How will the society encourage the continued growth and development of science and also the adoption of the results of science into innovative practice? That is the problem to which we address ourselves.

It is not a small problem. We live in an age in which science and technology research and development have been exploding. But there are very good reasons to think that the rate of growth may not continue to accelerate indefinitely into the future. Should science stop accelerating, there will arise in acute form the problem of providing an improved structure of incentives and rewards so as to maximize efficiency in R and D. An exploding science can afford inefficiencies in its direction which a scientific effort with limited resources cannot.

The conditions of scientific productivity is a subject about which we as social scientists know very little. Most of it deals with innovation, i.e., the adoption of a novel practice in use, rather than with pure discovery of things heretofore unconceived by the human mind. The lines between these two things are fuzzy; furthermore, we know little about the latter so in this paper we shall take the liberty of talking loosely about "innovation" meaning thereby either innovation strictly speaking or innovation and discovery combined and not distinguished. There is much research that is relevant to innovation, though not directly on the nose of our present subject. Social science has devoted a great deal of attention to the effects of technological

19

change on society. Social scientists have also devoted a good deal of attention to the social conditions of adoption of technological innovations. Social scientists have also given a good deal of attention to what makes a society modernize.

There are many significant theories in these peripheral areas. Forty years ago Max Weber developed an explanation for the development of modern capitalism in Western Europe—a phenomenon of entrepreneurial innovativeness if there ever was one—in which he attributed a primary causal role to the Calvinist ethic.[1] Certain religious ideological values led people to want to work regularly and to calculate the results of their work, and to keep on saving and investing.

More recently, David McClelland has developed a somewhat more rigorous model of the same phenomenon. He identifies a condition for innovative entrepreneurship as the presence of a certain personality syndrome which goes under the name of high need for achievement.[2] That again is associated with a desire to take small risks—not big risks; it is not a gambler mentality. It involves a desire to be able to calculate the risks and to act with a fair confidence of the outcome if one puts out effort.

So one set of social science writings have gone into the question of the kinds and distribution of certain personality types required for innovativeness in a society. Other social scientists have looked at the process of adoption of innovations that already exist elsewhere.

Everett Rogers has reviewed the literature on the diffusion of innovations, and also in his own research has contributed to identifying patterns by which an innovation that exists somewhere is adopted into a new milieu.[3] In any society certain types of people are the innovators, are fond of the new, try new things first. These individuals have certain specific characteristics. They tend to be younger, rather than older. They tend to be more highly educated than the norm. Partly for that reason they can seek out information in written sources. They read the journals, for example.

---

[1] Max Weber, *The Protestant Ethic and the Spirit of Capitalism* (New York: Charles Scribner's Sons, 1958).

[2] David C. McClelland, *The Achieving Society* (Princeton: D. van Nostrand Co., Inc., 1961).

[3] Everett M. Rogers, *Diffusion of Innovation* (New York: Free Press of Glencoe, 1962).

They also tend not to be the persons with maximum influence. An innovation comes to be adopted, Rogers finds, not as a result of their initial experiment with it, but rather when the innovation is later on tried out by a different kind of person, namely an opinion leader or community leader. These tend to be older, and tend to get their information orally rather than in writing. Because of their stature in the community they are followed by the rank and file, always leaving behind, of course, a few diehards who never adopt the new way.

Another aspect of the process of innovation which is much discussed in the literature is the question of the relationship of freedom to creativity. Until Sputnik was launched in 1957 you could have found many articles explaining that the Russians could never advance in science until Russian scientists obtained intellectual freedom. Then after 1957 you find much literature which said that they were moving ahead faster than any others in the world.

Perhaps we now have somewhat more balance on this issue, though less writing on it, because the issue seems less clear. We do not know exactly what it is, but there clearly is some relationship between freedom and scientific progress.

In the literature there are also very loose discussions of the role of leisure versus pressure. We are told that the creative scientist needs time to think, to be left alone, to engage in solitary daydreaming. There is a great deal to this.

On the other hand, we also know that technological innovation and scientific productivity generally tend to come out of extremely frenetic, extremely intense hothouses of activity. So there is another issue on which we are not very clear.

The literature also tells us that one of the social conditions for sustained technological growth is a critical mass of science. When there is a certain amount of activity that will generate more activity. When there are a certain number of scientists interacting with each other, new ideas emerge which generate further leads. So you get an exponential growth. That is a kind of contagion theory of the development of science.

An issue to which I shall address myself somewhat more, is the problem of rewards. There is fantasy that the scientist cares only about truth and beauty, or maybe even truth and not beauty. He is supposed to be doing research for its own sake and could not care less whether he is paid or not. That is a complete illusion. There is research data indicating that scientists are very concerned with such mundane things as money.

We do not have any very clear notions about the kinds of rewards that will achieve the purposes of stimulating science, i.e. the purpose for which the patent system was initially set up. It is not clear whether the pattern of rewards that grew up in the early years of science is appropriate to big science of today and whether it will continue to be appropriate to science as it evolves into an ever larger institution.

The patent system was designed at a period when the image of the inventor was that of the individual entrepreneur working in his workshop to invent an object which he would then take into the market to sell.

It was set up to reward the first producer of an item, in the hope that that would encourage more rapid introduction of innovation. A race would speed up the process of innovation. It was set up in the hope further of securing public knowledge of innovations, so you cannot receive a patent for a secret process.

The patent system was set up also in a way that provides no prize to the inventor as such. It provides an advantage in the market place for the entrepreneur who distributes the innovation. There is no reward for making an invention. There is merely a monopoly in marketing the product of the invention. Clearly the system that was set up by men whose image of the inventor was that of an inventor-entrepreneur, not merely an inventor.

In the meantime a great many changes have taken place in the process of invention, changes that I would like to review. They put in question whether the existing pattern of rewards is the most appropriate one that can be devised. Let us review some six significant changes that are taking place in the social environment of science.

1. In the first place, there has been a massive increase in the number of entrants into the scientific race. We described the process of winning a patent as that of winning a race to invent something first. There has been a tremendous increase in the number of people in this contest. By way of analogy we might think of the change as going from what was a simple, well-organized race with a few people running down a track, into a traffic jam. A large number of contestants are trying to pour through a narrow space not merely with the

speed of their own feet, but with the speed of powerful engines behind them.

Under these conditions the question of who is first is often a nonsense question. Many scientists work simultaneously on any problem of real importance. That has always been the case to some degree. The phenomenon of simultaneous discovery is extremely widespread in the history of science. Usually two, sometimes three, people made the same discovery within a matter of months or years. But it is no longer a matter of two or three people within a matter of months or years. It is now sometimes a matter of scores of people within a matter of days.

There is a journal put out by the physicists, the *Physical Review Letters*, which is designed specifically to provide almost newspaper speed reporting of new discoveries. And sometimes even it is too slow in this hectic race. When several institutions are working on the same measurement today, they will sometimes try to release the information to the newspapers in order to beat others out by a matter of hours.

Under these conditions, in which large numbers of people are working in an interactive network, all knowing that many other people are working on the same problem, and all racing for small margins of priority, one needs to raise the question whether it is the first invention that really should be the thing maximumly rewarded. Should not the goal of the patent system be rather speed of diffusion? What we want to reward is the adoption and utilization of new knowledge, not merely its first existence. What happens after its birth may have more effect on when it comes into effective use for society on a large scale.

2. A second major change, implied by the first one, is the growth of group research. That also raises a question as to who is to be viewed as the inventor. When research becomes an organized activity of a large number of people, who is to receive the reward? The growth of group research is developing rapidly in all fields.

3. A third major change is the organization of innovation. An invention today is seldom a surprise. To a large extent, we identify a purpose and then undertake an R and D program to find the means to achieve that purpose. Often there are several purposes that we wish to achieve that are hard to reconcile. If we optimize on one objective, we cannot optimize on another. R and D often consists in

working out a balance among such different goals any one of which is clearly achievable. The procedure in finding a solution is usually to assign to a team of scientists the job of developing a system or a device that will achieve the requisite balance.

This procedure is characteristic of defense research these days. One identifies a particular kind of operation that one would like to do better. One then identifies the broad parameters of a system that would achieve that. Then one sets teams to work to invent the required device.

Under such circumstances innovation becomes a business. The line between true invention and mere change becomes blurred. In the marketing field extensive organized innovation goes on all the time. Changes are deliberately planned and introduced in order to give the product characteristics that will make it desirable for the market.

Perhaps these are not changes of the same character as true scientific inventions, yet the line is hard to draw. Both are deliberately planned changes. One would like to reward not merely any change but those that constitute something that we might call progress. Unfortunately, nobody knows exactly what constitutes mere change and what constitutes progress. Yet somehow we might like to draw that line. We may not want to give monopolistic advantage merely for introducing a change that may have been made for no other purpose than that of gaining such a patent or copyright advantage.

If we are going to have innovation to order, then probably what we want to do is not just to reward the fact of innovation as such, but rather to reward the focus for the innovation. If we can innovate in any one of a myriad of directions, if we can innovate in design, if we can innovate in packaging, if we can innovate in quality, if we can innovate in the military field or in the civil field, if we can do this pretty much to order, according to where we want to put our emphasis and our effort, then is not the important thing to reward effort and emphasis put into the right place?

4. A fourth change of note has been the growth of sponsored research. Sponsored research is normally commissioned by people who are not themselves scientists. The scientist-entrepreneur who both invented a new product and also marketed it, may never have been the normal reality but he was certainly at one time the image of

the way applied science operated. He is certainly not even the image today. The image today is a scientist who is somehow under an administrator in an organization. Somebody in a bureaucracy has to make broad primary decisions about what the scientist or researcher will do. Another way of describing this situation is to say that the inventor today instead of working for a wide market of consumers is selling his services to a monopsony which administratively decides what it wants.

Some device has to be used to select inventions for adoption into use. Many ideas are conceived; few can be chosen. Some are rejected because they are poor, others because another alternative is chosen to do the same job. The old image was that the market provided the best device to select. Each innovation would be placed on the market, and if men found it an improvement, then a large number of them would buy it. If they did not find it useful, it would fail. Even in a market selection never fully works that way, for inventions are not independent entities but rather parts of systems. A better collar for dray horses will not be adopted in the market today.

Furthermore a large part of the product of research today must be chosen by some kind of collective decision, not by the market.

5. That will be increasingly so since one of science's frontiers in the coming period is the field of environmental control, i.e., the control of things that affect all of us simultaneously.

Weather control is a prime example. We cannot individually decide whether to have rain or sunshine. In the twenty-first century that will often be a social decision.

Medicine and public health is a field where we are already engaged in environmental control. We buy protection from epidemics collectively. The fact of contagion makes preventive action a social decision.

For a different reason the space program is collectively undertaken. Because of the magnitude of the investment required prior to the provision of transportation to the moon, we cannot make individual decisions on whether to go to the moon or not.

For still other reasons we will not be able to allow the control of genetics to remain a completely private matter when, in the twenty-first century we learn how to produce inheritable mutations. We will then presumably not allow experimenters to modify unborn human generations as they see fit. Man's ability to do that, when it occurs, will be more revolutionary and problematical for society than atomic energy has been in our lifetime.

So with science increasingly providing ways of modifying the entire human environment the choice among inventions becomes a collective decision. Correspondingly the reward for the scientist needs to be different from that which was the norm when the market was viewed as the ordinary test for innovations.

6. Finally, let me close my list of changes in the environment of science by suggesting that the overhead of science continues to grow and grow enormously. Anyone who is concerned with business, or even for that matter with university administration, knows what problems are created when overhead becomes an increasing percentage of the budget.

Derek de Solla Price, in an excellent book, *Little Science, Big Science*,[4] has estimated that in order to double the number of good scientists, you have to increase the total number of scientists by four. In other words, scientists increase as the square of the increase in the number of good scientists. If you want to get five times as many good scientists, you have to have 25 times as many scientists. He argues, I think less convincingly, that cost goes up by the fourth power: that if you want to develop double the number of scientists, then you have to increase the budget by sixteen, and so on.

This means that the scientific establishment grows much more rapidly than science itself. It means that the proportion of the gross national product devoted to R and D grows much more rapidly than does knowledge. It means that the increase in the number of people who have to be scientifically trained because they are going to be in technically related activities of one sort or another, also grows much more rapidly than does knowledge.

We have right now, depending upon whom you want to include, perhaps two million people engaged in R and D. How far can we increase that? Price estimates that it perhaps can go to eight million, to six to eight percent of the then labor force. A great many of the scientifically trained people will not be productive scientists. They include teachers, medical practitioners, and people on the administrative staffs of research departments. Those are people who have to have technical training, but that does not necessarily mean that they

---

[4] Derek de Solla Price, *Little Science, Big Science* (New York: Columbia University Press, 1963).

are adding to science. All of this useful overhead of science grows more rapidly than science itself.

If one is not careful overhead activity will increasingly eat into the research time of the creative scientist. If you look at the time budgets of what people do in a research institution today, you would find that even in top-flight research institutions, if the leading scientific people can devote 15 percent of their time to research they are doing well.

Actually, I think they are doing poorly. That is a miserably low figure, but it is a typical figure. They have to answer mail. They have to meet with their colleagues. They have to review grants or apply for grants. They have to go to meetings. They teach. They do all sorts of other things. The residual research time is likely to be on the order of 15 percent.

That is probably a much lower figure than it was for the smaller number of top scientists working half a century ago. They worked without the aid of the enormous overhead of research support that now exists, and that certainly limited them. But they probably had more time on their own. Society did not perceive that what they were doing was quite as important as we regard it today and so society left them alone. Scientists today pay for the organized activities and institutions that facilitate their work by committing time to administration and politics.

The six kinds of changes in the environment of science that we have listed are all continuing trends. They are going to become more marked in the years to come, but not forever. The exponential growth of science, for example, will soon present impossible problems. Clearly the exponential growth in the number of publications or the exponential growth in the part of gross national product going into science cannot continue indefinitely for at some point the total size of the publishing facilities and the total GNP set limits. Price, in his book, *Little Science, Big Science*, estimates that for most such variables, the doubling time is somewhere between ten and fifteen years. In other words, every ten to fifteen years we double the number of scientists, the number of publications, and so on. That has some interesting implications. One implication is that 80 to 90 percent of all the scientists who ever lived are alive today. As long as exponential growth continues, that will continue to be the case, because with each passing year we are producing so many more scientists. Scientists and engineers are increasing in numbers about three times as fast as the labor force as a whole. But this clearly cannot go on forever. No process can double every ten or fifteen years forever.

As we begin to run up against the inevitable ceilings to accelerating growth, we will confront many new problems. Consider the problem of rewards under conditions of restricted options. What kinds of rewards will produce selection of the desired options? A system of rewards that merely increases numbers of dollars or numbers of people devoted to research, no longer meets the needs, either because there are few more dollars or people to be directed into research or because increasing them penalizes other activities.

In a situation of scarce resources the key problem is that of choice: where to use the best men, to what should they address themselves. It is impossible to increase the number of top flight men exponentially indefinitely. Genius is one of the first bottlenecks. If we cannot increase it we must ration and allocate it.

This has already become an issue for the space program. Many scientists have argued that the moonshot is the wrong place to which to direct talent. Defenders of the program have argued that it uses mostly available engineers rather than scarce scientists. What concerns us here is not who is right but simply that there is such an issue. Since we now invent to order in any one of a large number of research fields, we must make decisions as to where our inventive energies should go.

The fact of scarcity of talent raises above all the question of how to keep productive scientists productive; how to prevent the productive 15 percent of their time from becoming ten percent or five percent; how to keep creative people creative for a longer portion of their life span.

It is well known that in many fields of science creation is done very early, that many scientists stop being creative after middle age. Also, successful scientists are transferred to administrative posts which carry higher prestige and higher salaries, but cut them off from making further major contributions. How can this be discouraged? What incentives will keep men productive and creative?

We know very little about the conditions that produce high scientific creativity, but we know something about it. There have been some extraordinary hothouses of scientific creation in the history of the world. A favorite example is ancient Athens. There are other more recent examples. One can identify the school in Budapest out of which in a single generation came Von Neumann, von Karmen, Teller, Szilard, and so on. We would like to understand the circumstances that created this hothouse, for apparently the multiplication of geniuses is possible. Unfortunately, we do not know how to produce such flowerings at will. We know a few things that are relevant. We know that a great deal of innovation consists of the transfer of knowledge from one field to another. Much invention is analogy. A classic example is Darwin's theory of evolution, which in many respects was simply a transfer to the biological world of certain Malthusian economic notions that were prevalent in England at that time. This is an unusual example, because it is a transfer from the social sciences to the natural sciences. Things usually go the other way, but they can go either way.

I have been trying to persuade some people recently that certain ideas in linguistics have important applications to traffic planning. This seems odd, but there are certain statistical techniques that have been developed in linguistics that are relevant to traffic engineering. This kind of transfer is a very large part of invention.

That fact suggests that one of the conditions for effective creativity is broad education and broad interaction among disciplines. The development of specialization which tends to come with the growth of the scale of science may not produce continued creativity.

The creative scientist tends to be distinguished from his less creative colleagues by his rejection of the frame of reference in which questions are posed to him. This has been established by a good deal of research, for example that of McKinnon in Calfornia. The man who is creative is apt to think about the same question as other people but to think about it in rather weird ways. He is likely to redefine the problem. If it is a spatial problem, to turn the object upside down or on its head.

One test that has proved to separate creative scientists involves drawing lines between points to meet specified criteria: the creative scientist tends to go off the page in solving the problem, which in fact is the right solution.[5] The redefinition of the frame of reference of the problem, very often by way of metaphor, characterizes creativity.

---

[5] Morris Stein and Jean McKenzie, Creativity Project Report, 1954, University of Chicago.

Jerome Bruner and colleagues studying a group of creative technologists have shown that creativity is in large part the presence of a
rather fertile fund of metaphors in the person's flow of fantasy.[6]

To have such fantasies requires not being too censorious of one's
self. The creative scientist tends to produce by this process of
fanciful metaphor a large number of rather absurd ideas, which he is
more willing to express in public than is the less creative scientist.
But of course, creativity also requires, at the appropriate point in
time, a willingness to reject many of these ideas as bad ones. But
premature censorship tends to stifle creativity.

So in assessing methods of reward we should ask what it does to
facilitate movement of people and knowledge between disciplines;
and what it does to facilitate an open, imaginative and free discussion
without too ready censorship. I am afraid that neither our patent
system nor our system of graduate education would score very high
by these criteria.

There is another question to which I wish to address myself in
closing, concerning the implications to society of the fact that science
cannot continue to expand exponentially. There is an issue among
predictors as to how many scientifically trained people we are going
to need. There are those who think that we are going to need a
tremendous increase in the number of educated people and other
good social scientists who say we are not. This is an old issue
discussed in the nineteenth century. Marx, for example, predicted
that the world was moving in such a way that more and more people
would do menial jobs on an assembly line and that the role of
complex skills would decline. It was this trend that was going to
make socialism possible. The trend would go to the point where it
would be so easy to run society that you would not need any
specialists at all. Everybody could do everything because the machines were going to do it all. Management and administration, in his
phrase, would be reduced to mere bookkeeping.

It has not worked out this way at all. On the contrary, there has
emerged what Daniel Bell describes as an intellectual technology.
The dominant roles in society, he says, are moving from those which

---

[6] Jerome Bruner, On Knowing: Essays for the Left Hand (Cambridge: Harvard
University Press, 1962).

required primarily entrepreneurship to ones that require primarily intellectual training of one sort or another.[7]

Bell, in other words, reverses the Marxist image of the future. He forecasts a society in which virtually everybody will be doing intellectual work.

I do not think that it is easy to say who is right and who is wrong or what the future will be on this point; but there certainly are important tendencies in the direction that Bell is indicating. Mankind started out with a hunting and then agricultural technology which required very high orders of skills. Most of us contemporary men, if we were thrown onto the countryside and told to run a productive farm, would be completely lost. There is an enormous amount of traditional knowledge about the particular environment that is needed to be a successful hunter or farmer. One needs to know a great deal about the particular place, the weather there, the soils there, the progression of life with the seasons. A tremendous body of lore goes into being a successful hunter, or fisherman, or farmer. In that respect these are highly challenging and creative jobs. It is true that the knowledge required is not knowledge that changes. One learns it in the process of growing up. One learns it from one's father. Nonetheless, to succeed one must learn a good deal.

The industrial revolution, as Marx indicated, greatly reduced the number of people who were doing that kind of creative job. A large number of people were given extremely simple jobs. The ability of the factory to use minimally trained people was an enormous asset. It made it possible for man to change his modest life from that of a static kind of society to that of a rapidly changing kind of society, a society in which change was itself institutionalized. Since men no longer needed to learn complex skills in childhood at the feet of their fathers, people could be born in one kind of world and live their adult lives in another kind of world.

One way to continue to have rapid change in society is to make the jobs that have to be done very simple. If we can break up work into modular units of very simple character, then a few planners, a few entrepreneurs, a few managers can shuffle things around and make the necessary changes. That was one of the great discoveries of the

---

[7] Daniel Bell, "The Post-Industrial Society," in Eli Ginzberg (ed.), *Technology and Social Change* (New York: Columbia University Press, 1964).

industrial revolution, but it is not clear that that path of progress remains open to us.

We have gone a further step now that changes the character of the industrial revolution. We have made it possible to automatize, to have the machine do almost any operation that can be done by a man in this modular routine fashion. So we have eliminated, or we are rapidly eliminating, the need for human beings to perform these routine functions at all. We face a situation now in which the jobs that need to be done are the creative jobs that require a high order of knowledge. In contrast to the skilled job of the farmer, or the fisherman, or the hunter, they require the use of a body of knowledge that is in constant flux.

The kind of man we have to create now is not merely a technically informed knowledgeable man, but one with an ability to learn quickly and to change quickly what he is doing. The new kind of man we need is one who is experimental, one who can work with general principles, and who is willing to permit the controlled play of fantasy which (as we noted before) constitutes a condition of creativity.

Here is society's dilemma. Our biological heritage has made the human being an organism capable of enormous knowledge and computational ability. But the human animal secures these powers at the expense of very long developmental and learning cycles. It takes roughly two decades to produce a mature human animal with all the habits and skills he needs to function as a full blown member of society. No other animal takes nearly that long. At the same time, the genius of this animal has produced a social environment in which many of the habits and skills learned by the individual humans are useful for less than the four or five decades that constitute the mature life of the organism. The first response to this dilemma was to invent modes of organizing work that required only very simple skills that could be quickly taught to a mature organism. This solution threw aside the potentialities that man could develop in his first two plastic decades and put lesser demands upon him. That solution has reached a dead end. It is obviously inefficient in that it uses nature's most marvellous machine for trivial functions that can be done better with dumber machines. Now we face the necessity of inventing ways to make mature organisms capable of unlearning and relearning and of doing so in shorter periods than the two decades of the initial developmental cycle. Some of the most important inventions of the next century are likely to be in the field of teaching and adapting the human organism to greater potentialities of learning and change. Much of what will be done will be done in the two decade developmental cycle to produce a more flexible, more absorptive product. Part of what will be done will be to invent better ways of teaching and motivating adults.

This prediction, like so many predictions, is likely to turn out to be true enough in the end if we attach no date to it. The issue on which Marx and Bell take opposite stands, and which I consider unresolved, is what the balance will be for any given decade in the future, the 1970's, 1980's, 1990's, between the two solutions to the dilemma, giving people highly simplified jobs or remaking them into creative technical innovators. It is not clear how many of each kind of person we will have need for in each decade.

We will certainly, however, need an increasing number of the latter kind of man, the creative technical man.

The problem of how to induce more men to work in this way is the difficult one to which we have in part been addressing ourselves in this discussion of incentives.

There is an erroneous superstition that creative, imaginative people need no other incentive than success in what they are doing. This wrong view says that the scientist cares only about truth for its own sake.

In some work by Stein and McKenzie at the University of Chicago, it was demonstrated that if you separated the less creative scientists from the more creative scientists, the more creative scientists were more interested in money as a reward.[8] It was the less creative scientists who talked about the progress of science as their reward. There are good reasons for this. The more creative scientist does tend to be more isolated from men in his value system. He has less need for affiliation, to use the psychological jargon, and more need for achievement. But to be sure that he has achieved that achievement, it must somehow be measured. Unless the scientist is rewarded in a measurable fashion he is not likely to be satisfied. He is not as

---

[8] Stein and McKenzie, *op. cit.*

satisfied by the praise and applause of a group around him as is a man who has more need for affiliation and is more person-oriented, less thing-oriented.

Let us close this essay in the fashion in which it originally closed when delivered as a talk. It closed with a relevant question from the audience.

QUESTION: The speaker has suggested that at least some of the problems with which we are faced now are not susceptible to entrepreneurial motivations, but should instead be socially motivated, and that we should have national goals set on some overall social basis. What success has been achieved in trying to arrive at planned social goals, and how do we avoid, if we can, having those dictated to us by a small group and enforced on the majority?

ANSWER: You want a quick answer to the biggest problem of our century.

It has always been true that science has responded in part to national goals. The work of Newton was in part responsive to the concern of the British Navy with finding a way to establish longitude. But there is a matter of emphasis. We are in a situation where a good many more of the things which are possible for science to do can only be done if a social decision is made. Now, you asked me how can we prevent that from leading to dictated social decisions by domineering authoritarian governments.

I can only reply that this is at least another several lectures. Nor have I an answer. I am not rejecting the question, but it is not a question to which I have a quick reply.

Does market structure have an effect on innovation? Economist Phillips examines the complex of relationships among market structures and the innovative and investment behavior of firms. In this context he develops a "go-no go" investment decision model for the firm, including some analysis of the dynamic relationships involved. He concludes that market structure, through its effects on rivalry, does have an effect on innovation. This effect is mixed, however, and generalization is difficult. Nevertheless, he does find that, generally, high rivalry encourages the innovation of products which are substitutes for existing products, whereas innovations of products complementary to existing products are consistent with low rivalry situations.

ALMARIN PHILLIPS is Professor of Economics and Law at the University of Pennsylvania. He attended the University of Pennsylvania where he received his B.A. and M.A. degrees and Harvard University where he received a Ph.D. He is a member of the Board of Governors of the Federal Reserve System, a consultant for the Rand Corporation and editor of the *Southern Economic Journal*. His publications include *Automation: Its Impact on Economic Growth and Stability, Problems in Basic Operations Research, Methods for Management* with R. W. Cabell, *Market Structure, Organization, and Performance,* and "Technological Change in Selected Manufacturing Industries," in the *Journal of Industrial Economics,* June 1956.

CHAPTER 3

MARKET STRUCTURE, INNOVATION AND INVESTMENT

> "Wish me good speed:
> For I am going into a wilderness
> Where I shall find nor path nor friendly clue
> To be my guide."
> Duchess of Malfi, I, i.[1]

The model developed below is an attempt to find a way through the complex of relationships among market structures and the innovative and investment behavior of firms. In many respects, the approach reflects no more than a collection and qualification of several hypotheses which have previously appeared. A general model is established for a "go - no go" investment decision by the firm. This model incorporates in a loose form the expected return from a "go" decision, the risk which is associated with the expected return because of cost and demand forecasting errors, and the risk which arises because of factors related to the structure of the market in which the firm exists.

Within the framework, the influences of market structure, of three types of investment projects, and of the relative sizes of firms on investment decisions are analyzed. In addition, some inferences are

* The author is indebted to T. K. Glennan, Jr., Richard R. Nelson, James R. Schlesinger, Oliver E. Williamson and Charles Wolf, Jr., who provided many helpful comments on an earlier draft. They are absolved of responsibility, of course.

[1] As quoted in R. M. Martin, "Performance, Purpose and Permission," *Philosophy of Science*, April, 1963.

37

drawn with respect to the timing and volume of investment spending in various market contexts. The combined treatment of all these factors leads to some notions of dynamic relations between innovation, investment and market structure and performance.

THE MODEL

The investment decision is viewed for a single firm at a particular point in time. This abstracts from the process through which firms receive or accumulate information concerning investment projects. It does not negate the possibility that the firm may have previously engaged in exploratory research or, should the project not be undertaken, that it will so engage itself in the future.

It is hypothesized that the willingness of an individual firm to undertake an investment project is related to the extent to which the project is expected to fulfill the goals of the firm, to the amount of risk which arises because of the nature of the project, the uncertainty of market demand, and other factors internal to the firm, and to the amount of risk associated with possible reactions from its rivals. In order more conveniently to refer to these factors, this propensity to make a "go" decision is expressed as:

$$(1) \qquad\qquad I = I(\bar{M}, S, D).$$

I can be thought of as an index of the combined strength of factors which favor the "go" choice. Alternatively, I could be defined as the probability which an observer of the investment decision would assign to the "go" choice. By presenting willingness to undertake a project in this fashion, problems associated with estimates of capital expenditures and the amount of investment are explicitly treated with consideration of the other variables. The expected level of goal achievement is represented by $\bar{M}$, S is the risk due to the factors internal to the firm and uncertainty with respect to total market demand, and D is the risk due to rivalry. Each of these will be explained in some detail.

The model is presented in an organizational and behavioral form. Thus, decisions are made in the context of "bounded rationality," firm goals may be of a "satisficing" sort, with the levels of goal attainment themselves conditioned by the market environment, and, to varying degrees which again depend on the market context, firms recognize their membership in a market group and the relations between their behavior and the performance of the entire group.[2] There is postulated, then, a complex structure of individuals within a hierarchy of organizations. The parts of this which lie within the formal organizations of the firms are important to the analysis to the extent that they influence the types of goals and goal-attaining behavior of the firms. The part of the structure which is more important to the analysis is the (usually) informal organization which exists among the firms in the market group and its influence on goals and behavior. It is assumed that this interfirm organization, in conjunction with other variables chief among which is the number of firms in the group, conditions the type and the degree of rivalry (conflict) among the firms.[3]

This view of the firm and the market affects the definition of $\bar{M}$ and S. For all firms, $\bar{M}$ relates to goal achievement for the firm itself. For some firms, $\bar{M}$ may be in terms of a monetary profit goal; for others, absolute or relative growth rates or the achievement of security may be the primary goal. As is developed below, differences in goals affect the willingness of firms to innovate and invest and may be systematically related to differences in market structure and the relative sizes of firms.

Because of the "go - no go" nature of the decision, $\bar{M}$ represents the

---

[2] J. G. March and H. A. Simon, *Organizations* (New York, John Wiley & Sons, 1958), especially Chap. 6. For related literature, see in addition: W. J. Baumol and R. E. Quandt, "Rules of Thumb and Optimally Imperfect Decisions," *American Economic Review*, March, 1964; H. A. Simon, "New Developments in the Theory of the Firm," *American Economic Review*, May, 1962; S. W. Becker and F. O. Brownson, "What Price Ambiguity? Or the Role of Ambiguity in Decision-Making," *Journal of Political Economy*, February, 1964; G. S. Becker, "Irrational Behavior and Economic Theory," *Journal of Political Economy*, February, 1962; I. M. Kirzner, "Rational Action and Economic Theory," *Journal of Political Economy*, August, 1962; E. H. Bowman, "Consistency and Optimality in Managerial Decision Making," *Management Science*, January, 1963; I. J. Good, "How Rational Should a Manager Be?" *Management Science*, July, 1962; H. T. Koplin, "The Profit Maximization Assumption," *Oxford Economic Papers*, July, 1962; A. Phillips, "Operations Research and the Theory of the Firm," *Southern Economic Journal*, April, 1962; R. M. Cyert and J. G. March, *A Behavioral Theory of the Firm* (Englewood Cliffs, N.J.: Prentice-Hall, Inc., 1963); and S. Siegel, "Level of Aspiration and Decision-Making," *Psychological Review*, July, 1957.

[3] A. Phillips, *Market Structure, Organization and Performance* (Cambridge: Harvard University Press, 1962), Chap. 2.

expected differential in the level of goal achievement from choosing
"go" as contrasted with choosing "no go." More specifically, $\overline{M}$ can be
defined as:

(2) $$\overline{M} = \overline{\pi}_1 - \overline{\pi}_2,$$

where $\overline{\pi}_1$ is the expected (and time discounted) value of goal
achievement for the "go" choice and $\overline{\pi}_2$ is a similar value for the "no
go" choice. The level of $\overline{M}$ for the individual firm depends, of course,
on its forecasts of $\overline{\pi}_1$ and $\overline{\pi}_2$. It is determined by a translation to goal
achievement variables of forecasts of market demand, estimates of
the share of this demand which will accrue to the firm, and estimates
of costs for both of the alternatives. Since it is necessary for analytic
purposes to keep separate the effects of rivalry on investment, these
forecasts and estimates and, hence, $\overline{M}$ are conceived of as expectations generated by the firm with certain knowledge of its rivals'
behavior and the effects of this behavior on $\overline{\pi}_1$ and $\overline{\pi}_2$.

Even in this construction, the choice of alternatives is not riskless,
however. Costs and total demand are not known with certainty. One
can think of $\overline{\pi}_1$ and $\overline{\pi}_2$ as means of the subjectively generated
probability distributions $P(\pi_1)$ and $P(\pi_2)$, respectively, and of these
distributions as having the variances σ^2_1 and σ^2_2. The latter are
measures of the risks pertaining to goal achievement connected with
the "go - no go" alternatives. The relevant factor for determining the
willingness to invest is the risk differential of the "go" choice, which
is defined as:

(3) $$S = \sigma^2_1 - \sigma^2_2.$$

Thus S, rather than being itself a measure of variance, reflects the
amount by which variance (risk) is increased (decreased) by the
selection of the "go" alternative. Given the risk of the "no go" choice,
S varies directly with σ^2_1, the risk of the "go" choice. For any value of
$\overline{M}$, increases in S raise the probability that the *actual* value of goal
achievement will be higher with the "no go" than with the "go"
choice. Similarly, increases in S raise the probability that the *actual*
level of goal achievement from the "go" choice will lie below a
minimally acceptable level.

The size of S depends primarily on the type of investment project
being contemplated. It could be negative if the investment involved
a shift from a "new" product with risky demand to an "old" product

with known demand, or a shift from a production function with unknown characteristics to a well-known production function. But these cases are neither typical nor interesting to a study of innovative behavior. Aside from them, S will tend to be lowest for expansions of capacity to produce existing products with existing technologies because of past experience with both production and marketing and the lack of required learning. That is, σ^2_1 and σ^2_2 are roughly equal. At the other extreme, S will tend to be highest for projects designed to produce new products with new technologies. If, for example, the project relates to a new product or process which entails a major advance in the state of technology or a product in which there has been little marketing experience, σ^2_1 will be much larger than σ^2_2. If the project is to produce existing products with a new, lower cost technology, S will tend to be higher than in the simple capacity expansion case, but lower than in the case in which even the product is novel.

To repeat, both $\overline{M}$ and S are defined as though the firm were certain of the effects of the behavior of rivals in each of the alternatives open to it. In reality, the effects of rivalry are known with more or less certainty. Moreover, the effects and the certainty of them may be different depending on whether the "go" or "no go" choice is elected. The purpose of the D variable is to account for these risks.

Rivalry depends primarily on the structural and organizational characteristics of the market. One aspect of the market organization is a system of communications (or interactions) among the firms which, as well as being instrumental in creating perceptions of "accepted" standards of behavior for the group, serves as the source of information concerning the extent to which the several firms adhere to the standards. That is, two levels of perceptions are involved. First, there are perceptions of an "accepted" code of market conduct—a pattern of behavior which, if followed by all, would be "good" for the collective group, though not necessarily for each of its members. In general, such perceptions tend to be more definite and to embrace more dimensions of behavior the smaller the number of firms, the more formal their interfirm organization and the more frequently they interact with one another. Because of its potentially strong impact on relations among firms, especially when their products are homogeneous, sanctions against price rivalry are common to virtually all perceived codes. In addition, the code relating to price behavior will tend to be better defined than are the codes concerning other types of behavior.

At the second level, the communications create perceptions of the frequency and type of violations of the code and, sometimes, of the sorts of stimuli which lead to these violations. Violations are more frequent the larger the number of firms, the less formal the interfirm organization and the less frequent the interactions among firms.[4] Again because of its importance, more attention is paid to price than to other aspects of behavior.

By definition, low rivalry occurs when the perceptions of the accepted code are clear to all firms *and* when each firm feels that the probability of others adhering to the code is high. High rivalry occurs when the perceptions of accepted conduct are ambiguous *or* when some firms feel that the probability of others adhering to the code is low. Depending on the behavioral dimensions selected, rivalry can be subdivided into classifications such as price, advertising, or innovative rivalry.

It follows that rivalry tends to be greater as the number of firms increases and the formality of the market organization decreases. When rivalry is very low, each firm recognizes that so long as it does nothing contrary to the accepted code, there is little probability that others will violate it. Thus, based on the (correct) assumption that each holds this view, a firm in a low rivalry market is relatively certain of future prices, outputs and market shares. Nonetheless, its behavior is constrained for, if the code were broken in a way which had significant impacts on the other firms, prices and outputs would be less certain because of the reactions of the others. Risk, then, is low so long as the contemplated action is within the "rules of the game," but high if the rules are breached.

As rivalry increases, this distinction is blurred. There is less certainty that all firms perceive the code clearly and less certainty that, even if they do, some firms will not act in a way which will "upset" the existing price and market share structures. As rivalry increases, the individual firm can be less certain of the future condition of the market, but the amount of uncertainty becomes less and less dependent on its own behavior. While firms in low rivalry markets will tend to avoid decisions which would create market

---

[4] G. Stigler, "A Theory of Oligopoly," *Journal of Political Economy*, February, 1964.

uncertainty, firms in high rivalry markets have no such constraint on behavior. Regardless of what the latter do, market uncertainty will remain.

The D variable reflects the degree of risk associated with rivalry for the "go" choice. In the low rivalry case, D is low so long as the investment project under consideration falls within the market code of behavior. Stated alternatively, D would appear high to a firm in an existing low rivalry situation if the "go" decision portended strong reactions from other firms. As rivalry increases, the behavior of other firms becomes less dependent on whether the decisions made by a *particular* firm are consistent with the code. In high rivalry, the performance of the market is uncertain regardless of the decision and, because of this, D will tend to be high. It is possible, nonetheless, that there will remain differences in D between the "go" and "no go" choices in the high rivalry situation. If, for example, the "go" choice involves a form of product differentiation which isolates the firm from the rest of the market, D may be lower for it than for the "no go" choice. In this case, uncertainty remains in the "go" alternative with respect to how others will behave, but there is less uncertainty with respect to the effects of this behavior on the firm exercising the choice.

Returning to the model, it is assumed that:

$$(4) \qquad \frac{\partial I}{\partial \overline{M}} \geq 0; \frac{\partial I}{\partial S} \leq 0; \frac{\partial I}{\partial D} \leq 0.$$

The first of these conveys only the conventional notion that the willingness to invest is directly related to the expected return. The relationship is written to allow the partial derivative to be zero when, despite high values for $\overline{M}$, high values for S or for D dictate a "no go" choice. The negative partial relations between I and S and between I and D reflect the "Fellner hypotheses."[5] These incorporate safety and risk aversion factors in the investment decision.

Before turning to an attempt to interrelate the several influences that have been traced, it seems that generalizations with respect to firm goals and the structure of markets are possible. In the low rivalry case, especially when the number of firms is small, the clear percep-

---

[5] W. Fellner, *Competition Among the Few* (New York: Alfred A. Knopf, Inc., 1949).

tions of behavior codes and the equally clear perception that the decisions of each firm have significant effects on all firms lead each to identify strongly with the market group. So long as market demand conditions are favorable enough so that all firms can simultaneously achieve their individual goals, behavior tends towards that which preserves the existing distribution of gains among the firms. None is impelled to gain relative to the others because of the existing satisfactory situation. Here, the goals of all firms are apt to emphasize security, and decisions which threaten security will tend to be avoided even when the probability of higher monetary gains is good. Decreases in demand would, of course, make the existing condition seem less secure and increase the relative importance of monetary gain for each firm.[6]

Moving from this extreme of virtually no rivalry, firm goals reflect interactions between the over-all degree of rivalry in the market and the relative position of the individual firm. When the number of firms is small and differences in relative sizes exist, all firms may clearly perceive of their interrelationships but their goals will tend to differ. The larger the firm, the less will be the desire to grow relative to the others and the greater will be the desire to have all firms behave to insure security. Smaller firms, on the other hand, will be more interested in growth relative to the market and less sensitive to (or aware of) the motive of security. The behavior of the large firms tends, in fact, to keep the market risk of the smaller firms less than it would otherwise be.

As the number of firms and, hence, rivalry increases, several coincident changes affect firm goals. Since individual firms are both less conscious of and less able to influence the performance of the group as a whole, goals tend to emphasize the absolute performance of the firm, not its performance relative to others. To the extent that security is included in firm goals, its achievement depends more on individual action to isolate the firm from the group since, as rivalry increases, the probability of successful group action diminishes.

---

[6] Market demand is singled out as the chief factor within the "munificence of the external environment" elements, though it is by no means the only one. As demand decreases, actual achievements tend to fall short of aspired or satisfactory achievements, and rivalry is stimulated. Cf. March and Simon, *op. cit.*, pp. 119–120. I prefer this explanation to the MC = MR explanation because of the oligopolistic interdependence assumed in the model. In addition, it can be used to cover other environment elements such as monopsonistic pressures on the group, interindustry competitive effects, and so on.

Finally, if high rivalry persists over a period of time, the poor performance—from the point of view of the firms—affects the aspirations of many in the group. They tend to become resigned to low levels of achievement and to fail to recognize alternatives which offer higher achievement. It should be expected, however, that those firms which, because of either chance or good management, had been the more successful would experience this less. The latter would typically be the larger firms in the group and these, it is conjectured, may have higher levels of aspiration.

In summary, greater rivalry suggests more attention to the goals of individual firms and more willingness to ignore the effects of decisions on others. But since rivalry affects general market performance and performance affects the desire to achieve, it is felt that the smaller firms will have higher aspirations for individual achievement in low rivalry markets. Conversely, the market environment tends to cause the larger firms to have the higher aspirations in high rivalry markets. The position of the firm within the market as well as the general level of rivalry is thus another factor to consider in generalizing about the willingness to invest.

MARKET STRUCTURES, FIRM SIZE, AND TYPES OF INVESTMENT EXPENDITURES

It is necessary at this point to categorize market structures and degrees of rivalry even though in actuality the variations in structure and rivalry form continue. The categories erected are: (1) monopoly or highly collusive oligopoly, (2) loosely collusive oligopoly, and (3) high rivalry markets. Within each of these, three general types of investment projects will be discussed from the points of view of large and small firms.

Monopoly or Highly Collusive Oligopoly

This structure is intended to cover the minimum degree of rivalry. In the single firm monopoly variant, the only sources of conflict are internal to the firm and the remote competition of other goods which, by definition, are poor substitutes. In highly collusive oligopoly, conflict among the firms is assumed to be similar to that within the monopoly firm. The group, at least initially, is considered to be in equilibrium in the sense that each of the participating firms, by adhering to perceived standards of behavior, receives benefits from participation which exceed the value of the contribution which continued membership implies. Assuming that market demand is strong enough so that the internal goals of all firms are being satisfactorily met, there is little in the external environment to induce conflict. A consciousness develops that the individual firms should do nothing which would upset the existing status quo. At the extreme, then, there is neither price nor opponent-specific types of non-price rivalry in the highly collusive oligopoly.[7]

In these conditions, the willingness of firms to invest in capacity expansions for existing products with existing technology (Type I_a expenditures) is primarily a function of $\overline{M}$. The value of S is low because of the type of project; that of D is low so long as the expansion being contemplated does not threaten the relative positions of the several firms in the market. As demand increases, $\overline{M}$ values for the firms increase, and the model suggests that the firms would be willing, in parallel fashion, to expand capacity promptly.

The promptness of the investment response may obscure what from another point of view is less favorable, however. Among the highly collusive oligopolists and within the monopoly firm, there is awareness that sustained goal achievement requires the avoidance of excess capacity for the group as well as the avoidance of significant changes in the relative capacities within the group. Should investment increase capacity more rapidly than demand rises, the goals of firms would be less satisfactorily met, and rivalry would be stimulated. Thus, the "code" of behavior will call for caution with respect to the volume of investment even if the timing is prompt.[8]

The above results are the more pertinent if entry is barred by patents or other means. If entry is relatively easy, the monopoly or highly collusive oligopoly may be both more willing to expand and more anxious to invest an amount capable of supplying enough

---

[7] This is, of course, a matter of definition. Both the degree of collusion and the absence of interindustry competitive effects which have been postulated may be rare.

[8] For an illustration of such a code, see "Optimistic Chemical Executives Get Warning on Overexpansion," *New York Times*, June 12, 1964, p. 47. In this case, however, the code was apparently being violated and fears were expressed that prices would fall because of it. See "Optimistic Chemists—Chemical Firms to Put Record $1.8 Billion Into New Facilities in 1964," *Wall Street Journal*, July 14, 1964, p. 1.

goods to satisfy demand at prices which are entry-preventative. Otherwise the monopoly or the effectiveness of the oligopolistic organization will be threatened by the emergence of new firms. The prevention of substantial entry barriers would in this instance play an important role in bringing about more socially desirable investment and pricing behavior.

Analysis of projects intended to produce new products with new technologies (Type I_b expenditures) is more complicated. The risk factor, S, is high relative to that for non-innovative expansion. Prospective values for $\overline{M}$ depend not only on anticipated demand and costs for the new product, but also on the demand for the old and relations between the two. Complete analysis involves this demand interdependence.

The new product may be either a substitute for or a complement to older products on the demand side. If it is a substitute, its introduction will tend to reduce the demand for the older products of the innovating firm and of others in the group. This will tend to make the *net* value for $\overline{M}$ low despite the possible existence of a high return on the new product itself. In addition, if the innovation has differential effects among the firms, its introduction may be viewed as a violation of the code, in which case D would seem high. These factors tend to retard innovation, especially if the demand for the older products promises to fulfill aspired achievement goals during the foreseeable future and if S is high because of technological, cost and time risks associated with the new product. In all these circumstances, there is a motivation to "bury" technological developments rather than to introduce them—a motivation to retain the security of the status quo.[9]

On the contrary, if the new product is complementary to existing products, the net $\overline{M}$ from simultaneously producing both may be higher than the sum of returns from both when considered in isolation from one another. The introduction of the new will tend to increase the demand for the old and, very possibly, to reduce the elasticity of that demand. If the innovation is not "tied" to the older product of the innovating firm, other firms may share in these

---

[9] The unwillingness of firms to introduce new and substitute products sometimes continues in the face of obvious threats to the security of the status quo. Producers of steam locomotives refused to replace their own products with diesel locomotives even after it was clear to others that there would be little future market for the steam variety.

demand increases. In any case, the complementary innovation should have a smaller effect on D than does a substitute innovation. It appears, therefore, that the monopolistic or highly collusive oligopolistic structure will tend to encourage innovation in complementary products. Nonetheless, the volume of investment for the production of these goods would still fall short of what might occur with increased rivalry.

Some qualifications concerning the apparent reluctance of monopoly and highly collusive oligopoly firms to invest for substitute products are obvious. First, if the technology is known to outsiders and is not protected by patents or other entry barriers, the motivation for entry is high. The incoming firm has no market in the older products to lose and, hence, its evaluation of $\bar{M}$ will tend to be higher than that of firms already in the market. At the same time, it is possible that the potential entrant would entertain higher values for S and for D than would the existing firms because of its lack of production and marketing experience and the uncertainty about how the older firms would behave if entry occurred. It appears that the effect of patent protection for the existing firms is to retard innovation by others without adding any inducement for the existing firms to innovate. Patent protection for the firm entering a market with a new substitute would tend to raise its $\bar{M}$ value—and to lower its values for S and D. In the latter case, innovation via entry would be encouraged by the patent.

A second qualification concerning the introduction of substitute products involves relations within a highly collusive group. The firm which recognizes the possibility of innovation first will be motivated to break from the group, especially if it is a smaller firm for which the innovation offers possibilities of growth and if through patents or other devices it can prevent the others from following. The collusive group equilibrium is threatened because the innovation tends to create a situation in which continued participation by this firm involves greater contributions than benefits. If it can introduce the product and prevent the others from following, it may capture much of the market of its former associates while losing only its share of the market for the older product.

It is difficult to be specific about the extent to which patents would encourage innovating firms to break from the highly collusive group. If firms in such groups tend to behave in a satisficing manner, it can be argued that the breaking away is more apt to occur when the demand and cost conditions for older products are such that the minimally acceptable levels of performance are being threatened. Otherwise, there is little pressure to exit from the group. Alternatively, it can be argued that the value for D will be higher in these circumstances; the other firms will react strongly—lowering prices for the old product and attempting to "invent around" the patent barrier—not only because of the threats to their own goal achievement but also as an emotional reaction to the violation of accepted behavior by the innovating firm.[10]

Patent pools among highly collusive oligopoly firms are one means by which the group can be kept collusive through time. When fully operable, such pools eliminate the tendency for group disequilibria to occur from innovations of new products and the analysis reverts to that for the single monopoly firm. It seems likely that patent pools arise as a response to the experience of firms breaking from the group because of product innovations. Repeated occurrence of this—first by one firm and then another—would lead to the realization that more "rational" innovating behavior would be mutually beneficial.

Investment expenditures for cost reducing purposes (Type I_c expenditures) can be treated in more orthodox fashion. The $\overline{M}$ values will be positive for any project in which total costs with the new technology, including development costs, are less than variable costs with the old over the relevant planning horizon. Because of S values, the new technology may not be introduced unless the $\overline{M}$ is relatively high and the probable value of adverse outcomes is correspondingly small. But for such projects, the value for D should be low since there is no direct market impact from the innovation on the performance of other members of the highly collusive group. Patent protection serves as a barrier to entry by firms utilizing a new technology and thus as a barrier to rivalry and lower prices.

It can be conjectured that where S is large, there will be disinclination in existing firms to pursue cost reducing innovations so long as demand is adequate to assure that aspired achievement levels will be met. When demand conditions pose an external threat to achieve-

---

[10] It seems less likely, but a similar motivation to break from the group could arise from the innovation of a product complementary to the old one. If a single firm can introduce such a product and "tie" it to only its old product, it may succeed in differentiating its old product from that of the other firms so as to capture a substantial share of their demand.

ment, cost reducing innovations may be encouraged and, again, the successful firm may be inclined to break from the group with price reductions which reflect the attainment of its own goals with the lower costs. This is simply another aspect of technical change leading to group disequilibrium.

Loosely Collusive Oligopoly

In this type of market, firms have clear perceptions of a code for price behavior. The more homogeneous the products, the more definite will this code tend to be. The code does not preclude the achievement of individual goals through nonprice rivalry. Indeed, in some case rivalry through advertising or product innovation may be explicitly "accepted" forms of behavior. The firms generally refrain from price rivalry, but perceive that price rivalry may occur when individual members of the group regard it as being to their own advantage. This type of market might be called the "Baumol structure,"[11] with price-constrained efforts at output or market share growth. It is assumed, however, that the larger firms are less interested in relative growth than are the smaller firms and that the former behave and extoll others to behave so as to achieve greater market security.

The greater importance of individual firm goals—especially by the smaller firms in this structure—implies that the group price equilibrium is less stable than that of highly collusive oligopoly. The equilibrium situation entails a price which is above the long-run marginal costs of the member firms, but because of the less formal organization and a less efficient communication system, the equilibrium can be upset by changes in the environment external to the group or by changes in relative achievement within the group.

Type I_a expenditures for simple capacity expansion have lower S values than do innovative investment projects. Because of the less efficient communication system and, perhaps a larger number of sources of information, demand forecasts have greater risk in this type of market structure than in the monopoly case, leading to somewhat higher S values even for non-innovative expansion.

As in the monopoly-highly collusive oligopoly case, increases in demand lead to higher $\overline{M}$ values. The response to this may be

[11] W. Baumol, *Business Behavior, Value and Growth* (New York: Macmillan Co., 1959).

delayed, however, because of the higher values for D in this case. The rivalry for shares creates in each firm the (correct) perception that when one expands the others will follow. Since competitive investment for capacity may cause a condition of over-supply, the investment decision is made in conditions of uncertainty with respect to whether the eventual outcome may not lead to price cutting.

The speculation, then, is that non-innovative investment by loosely oligopolistic firms will be sporadic. With initial increases in demand, investment may lag because of the combination of low $\overline{M}$ values and high D values. As demand continues to increase, $\overline{M}$ values increase and there is a tendency for the D values to decrease as the danger of excess capacity subsides. At some point, one firm leads off with expansion, rapidly followed by the others. Whether or not this leads to over-capacity and price rivalry depends generally on the extent to which the firms' goals for market share increases are constrained by recognition of the need for joint goal achievement. The less formal the organization, the more likely it is that a group disequilibrium (i.e., price rivalry) will occur.[12]

The influence of free entry is to improve investment performance so far as the timing of initial capacity expansion is concerned. Expansion to meet demand may be as important as entry-preventative pricing in forestalling entry when demand increases. With free entry, investment for capacity expansion will be made by newcomers—and at the expense of the market shares of existing firms—if the existing firms do not respond quite promptly. But while free entry may improve the initial timing of investment, it may also aggravate the tendency to cyclical over-investment in such markets.

Again, the analysis of the Type I_b projects is more complicated. Values for S are higher than for other types of investment, and the more radical the change in products and technology, the higher will these values be. Both $\overline{M}$ and D values depend in part on the type of innovation—whether it is a substitute or complement for existing products—and on whether others in and out of the group can easily duplicate the innovation.

---

[12] Thus, in contrast with the pre-World War II behavior of Alcoa as a monopolist, the loosely oligopolistic industry of the 1950s got into what in this context appears to have been open competition for capacity and market shares. In the late 1950s, when demand failed to grow as fast as capacity, ingot prices broke. When output again approached capacity in 1964, the firms were far more cautious to avoid repetition of the experience. That is, they were constrained by the joint goal achievement objective. See "Creeping Capacity—Aluminum Firms Draft Plans to Expand Again, But at a Snail's Pace," *Wall Street Journal*, July 6, 1964, p. 1.

When firm goals are associated with market shares and output in loosely collusive oligopoly, the $\bar{M}$ values for innovative substitutes for existing products may appear high.[13] The greater the extent to which rivals and new entrants can be foreclosed, the higher will the $\bar{M}$ value for the innovating firm appear. Patents, in this context, may stimulate innovation, especially among growth oriented smaller firms. Rivals, on the other hand, are more likely to react in ways contrary to perceived norms of behavior the greater are the inroads on their demand from the new product. Thus, the more successful is the innovation in capturing a large share of the market, the higher will the D value appear. Introduction of the new product may lead to price-cutting, efforts at competitive innovation, infringement suits, etc. This may, but need not, deter the firm from introducing the product. If rivals are prevented from easily duplicating the innovation or if the innovation tends to insulate the firm from the reactions of rivals, the D value is small for the "go" decision of the innovating firm even though its actions may create rivalry among the others. This may lead to a general pattern of successive efforts at production innovation among all the firms, with each feeling persistent pressure continuously to innovate in order to keep its products differentiated from others.

Should the market become disorganized as a result of a successful innovation by one firm, efforts are likely to arise to reorganize the market and to prevent reoccurrence. The reorganization might involve agreements to share or to delay the introduction of substitutes, at least during the period when demand for the old product continues high. Less formally, it is possible that without agreement a pattern of gradual product change would arise.[14]

If the innovation of a complementary product is not "tied" to the existing products of the innovating firm, it tends to increase the

---

[13] Note, however, that an increase in market share cannot be the sole criteria for $\bar{M}$. Innovations which increase market share but which reduce profits below minimally accepted standards would have low $\bar{M}$ values.

[14] Perhaps this is what has transpired in automobile and major appliance markets. In the former, model changes did lead to price cuts in the early years. Gradually the behavior of firms was regularized, and the customary practice of making "major" changes in models every three years and "minor" changes in the other two years arose. The very practice of having annual models reflects a pattern of group behavior with respect to innovation. See Hans Brems, "Response Lags and Nonprice Competition with Special Reference to the Automobile Industry," in *Expectations, Uncertainty and Business Behavior* (New York: Social Science Research Council, 1958).

demand for all firms in the group. This implies that D values will be low but, especially for the smaller firms whose goals are associated with market shares, so are the $\overline{M}$ values as compared with what would exist if a successful "tie" could be achieved. Patents and tying devices may thus stimulate innovation by increasing the $\overline{M}$ values for complementary products.

The freedom of new firms to enter the market with a new product would tend to hasten the introduction of both substitute and complementary products. If the existing firms do not do it, new ones may, with adverse effects on market shares and dangers of market disequilibrating tendencies. This potentiality can lead to joint efforts to prevent entry. Just as entry preventative pricing may emerge without formal agreement, so may entry preventative product innovation occur. Here, new products would appear more rapidly than would otherwise be the case. From the point of view of the existing group, however, complex patent cross-licensing and other jointly arranged barriers to entry are a preferable alternative. This provides motivation, then, for a more formal and collusive market organization.

As in the monopoly case, type I_c projects for cost reductions have little connection with rivalry save as a "safeguard" device should price rivalry arise. Positive $\overline{M}$ values depend on the condition that total costs with innovation are less than variable costs with the old technology. In the monopoly case, it was conjectured that so long as satisfactory goal achievement was being attained with the old technology there would be little pressure to innovate cost reducing technologies even where $\overline{M}$ is positive. In the case of loosely oligopolistic firms, the higher values for D make occasional price rivalry more likely and, hence, make long-run goal achievement more dependent on efficient production. The "insurance" aspect of cost reducing innovation, which has little short-run effect on rivalry itself, would appear to provide more motivation in the loose oligopoly situation.

High Rivalry Markets

High degrees of rivalry are characteristic of markets in which there is a combination of relatively large numbers of sellers and weak organizational restraints on firm behavior. Both of these conditions are necessary. On the one hand, the effect of large numbers can be offset by a formal market organization;[15] on the other hand, a very small number of sellers can be highly collusive with a very informal organization. The existence of high rivalry does not negate the proposition that communications among firms tend to develop perceptions of conduct standards, but because of the number of firms, the informal organization and the less efficient communication system, the perceptions may not be clear and individual firms may require little inducement to breach the code. The firms so often find circumstances in which the contribution involved in adherence to the code exceed the benefits that the group is in frequent disequilibrium. If the firms are producing a homogeneous product which by its nature does not permit innovative product differentiation, the rivalry may at times become acute.

In terms of the investment model, the outstanding characteristic of high rivalry markets is the high value for D for any projects save those which involve major product differentiation. This is fortified by experience in the market, in which the failure and turnover rates for firms tend to be high.[16] As developed above, it is assumed that this environment influences the aspirations of firms in the market. For some of the firms, the high degree of uncertainty, the inability to control the market perceptibly, and poor levels of performance decrease aspired achievement goals. The smaller firms typically persist in a desire to remain in the market, yet behave in ways which assure low levels of future achievement. This may in part reflect lack of knowledge about or ability to shift to alternative pursuits, but the effects of the environment on aspirations and a consequent failure to search for alternatives seem more important.

For other firms—usually a numerical minority of larger firms—the effect of the uncertain and low achievement environment is the reverse. High achievement goals are set and such firms are willing to subject themselves to high risk in order to attain them. These same firms are usually more conscious of group goals for the whole market

---

[15] While it is usually very difficult to develop privately so formal an organization that high collusion results with large numbers of sellers, it is not impossible. Consider, for example, the use of multiple basing points by the pre-1948 cement industry or the activities of unions in price setting for barbers' services.

[16] This is virtually a sine qua non for high rivalry. Turnover of group membership contributes to the continued existence of high rivalry. Absent free entry, failures and consolidations of existing firms—due to the rivalry—causes the number of firms to decrease, an internal power structure to emerge, and more homogeneous values to develop among the firms. The end result is less rivalry.

and, when achievement through product innovation is barred by the nature of the product, engage in efforts to organize the market more formally. The latter efforts, it should be noted, are frustrated more often by the behavior of the firms whose achievement goals are low and who have little awareness of the group than by conditions of the external environment.[17]

In high rivalry markets, type I_a investment behavior by existing firms is notable chiefly because of the lags involved. The firms with low achievement goals do not attempt expansion. Firms with high achievement goals, displaying an awareness of relations between group performance and individual achievement which is akin to that of oligopolists, initiate communications which warn of the dangers of capacity creation and over-supply.[18] Through the initial phases of demand-increases these communications, in conjunction with the high D value and the higher values for S which the market structure entails, retard capacity expansion by the high aspiration type firm. The result is that, compared with more oligopolistic markets, prices increase more and output increases less during the early phases of increases in demand.

The price rise, of course, gradually leads to capacity expansion. Some of the existing firms expand and, often more important, new firms enter the market. When the changes in demand are cyclical, the result may be that actual capacity expansion occurs near cyclical peaks, accentuating the distress conditions and the reductions in price which accompany the decreases in demand.[19] Secular tendencies to change this performance exist, but the effectiveness of them depends on whether the products of the firms can be differentiated and on their success in barring entry and gradually eliminating the low achievement type firms.

Type I_b expenditures for new sorts of products are extraordinarily attractive for the high achievement firms in high rivalry markets. Whether the innovation is a substitute or complement with respect to older products, its introduction tends to be uninhibited by the possible reactions of rivals—rivalry for existing products is at an

---

[17] But public policy, as one aspect of the external environment, may prohibit types of behavior which are effective in formalizing the market organization, especially when the result of the behavior is predatory with respect to the low achievement type firms.

[18] Cf. *American Column and Lumber Co.* v. *U.S.*, 257 U.S. 377 (1921).

[19] The behavior of the lumber and bituminous coal industries was illustrative, at least up to 1940.

extreme by assumption. Moreover, successful product differentiation is the means to reduced market uncertainty and, hence, to more satisfactory goal achievement for the firm. While the individual firm may be unable to affect rivalry in the entire market, an innovation which insulates it from the market would have a low D value. In this sense, increases in rivalry tend to develop pressures for innovation within individual firms as a means of reducing uncertainty and achieving higher goals.

There is one difficulty, however. Markets in which high rivalry exists over long periods of time seem uniformly to be those with products which are not susceptible to major product innovation and differentiation. Where this is not the case, successful innovation leads to the rapid growth of one or a few firms—a selection of the high achievement firms—and to the rapid demise of the others. The result of type I_b projects is thus to change the market structure, moving it towards the oligopoly or monopoly case. It is anticipated that high rivalry will remain over long periods only in those markets in which the nature of the product cannot be changed.[20]

Type I_c projects are also attractive to the high achievement type firm in the high rivalry market. In fact, when product innovations are impossible, cost reducing innovations are the principal vehicle by which better achievement goals can be attained, and the larger, high achievement firms tend to make them. It is possible that success in such innovations will also lead to changes in market structure and, secularly, to lower D values as firms with higher costs are forced from the market. This tendency is mitigated by the differences in aspirations, however, and unless the cost reduction is a major one, the existing, low-achievement type firms may elect to remain despite their poor performance.

SUMMARY AND CONCLUSIONS

Simple generalizations about relationships between market structure and innovation are, it is clear, both inadequate and hazardous. Unfortunately, while those in the present paper are more complex than many which have appeared, they rest on the most fragile sort of

---

[20] This is a necessary but not a sufficient condition for sustained high rivalry, as should be clear from the previous emphasis on organization, firm turnover and barriers to entry.

behavioral assumptions and, even then, fail to explain much of the problem. But with these caveats, some conclusions do emerge.

Market structure, through its effects on rivalry, appears to have a mixed effect on innovation. As rivalry tends to subordinate group goal achievement relative to achievement for the individual firm, it tends to stimulate innovation. But, as rivalry tends through its effects on performance to reduce aspirations for achievement, it retards innovative activity. This interaction differentially affects firms of varying sizes, stimulating innovation among smaller firms when rivalry is low and among larger firms when it is high. Moving from the low rivalry extreme, it may be that the result in the entire market is first a positive one on over-all innovative activity and subsequently a negative one. That is, solely from the innovation point of view, there may be an "optimum" degree of rivalry somewhere between the extremes.[21]

The analysis suggests that the timing of investment for changes in capacity may be better at the monopoly-low rivalry end of the spectrum than it is when rivalry is high. The volume of such investment seems to vary directly with rivalry, however, tending to be inadequate from the conventional view of monopoly behavior at the one extreme and, perhaps, to be excessive when rivalry is very high.

In general, rivalry encourages the innovation of products which are substitutes for existing products, though observations of actual markets may obscure this tendency because of differential effects by size of firm and because the products of firms in many high rivalry markets do not lend themselves to product innovations. Innovations of products complementary to existing products need not be impeded by low rivalry except as the latter is associated with such effective goal achievement that the desire to improve performance is reduced. Related to this is the general conclusion that as the demand for existing products falls and goal achievement reduced, the pressure to innovate, given the degree of rivalry, is increased.

Finally, there is the obvious conclusion that additional empirical research is required. But there is little likelihood that the factors which relate market structures to innovation and investment can be

---

[21] See Oliver E. Williamson, "Innovation and Market Structure," *Journal of Political Economy* (February, 1965), p. 63, for an empirical test with results which are consistent with this hypothesis.

easily quantified. Firms can be counted, but this does not measure rivalry. Output per unit of input can be estimated, but this does not measure technological change. The research, if successful, will require bold techniques to assess the significance of various sorts of market organization, of various degrees of substitutability and complementarity among products, of various aspirational effects, of different sources of innovative pressure, and of the various degrees of advance in technology. None of these is easy to handle in an empirical way and none of us should be surprised if most empirical studies, by failing to include them, produce few positive results.

Besides the influence of industrial growth, the social environment, and market structure, what is the role of the patent system in stimulating technical change? Three contributors consider the significance of patent rights. Attorney Frost treats the basic theory of the patent system and then considers the limitations of patent rights in stimulating the creation of technology. He also discusses legal problems regarding patents. In spite of the problems and limitations of the patent system, Frost concludes that it will continue to have an important role in encouraging business to create technology.

GEORGE E. FROST is a partner in Frost, Burmeister and Kulie law firm in Chicago. He attended Illinois Institute of Technology and George Washington University where he received his law degree. He is director of the Patent Division, Lawyers Institute, and Instructor in Patent Law, a member of the Attorney General's National Committee to study Anti-trust laws, and a member of the American Patent Law Association. His published writings include *Patent Infringement and the Public Interest*, *Legal Incidents of Non-Use of Patented Inventions Reconsidered*, *Misuse as a Per Se Violation*, and *Patent Office Performance in Perspective*.

CHAPTER 4

PATENT RIGHTS AND THE
STIMULATION OF
TECHNICAL CHANGE

George E. Frost

✦The roots of the patent system may be traced to early Greek civilization.[1] Since at least the seventeenth century, the issuance of patent rights has been accepted as a way to stimulate inventive effort.[2] Since these beginnings, the economy has been completely transformed. The industrial revolution of the 18th century initiated factory production and the substitution of machine for human and animal power. Organized scientific research was initiated in the late nineteenth century in the chemical and electrical fields, giving rise to an unprecedented technological growth in these fields. We now have machinery for control and computation purposes, as well as further advances in mechanical, chemical, and electrical technology that make the economy of the 1960's quite unlike that of even a generation ago. And the only thing that can be said with certainty as to the future is that there will be continued technical change.

The patent system has likewise changed. Some changes have resulted from changes in technology. Other patent system changes have come as the result of the increased magnitude of research and development effort. Still other changes have come as defects in the patent system itself have become apparent. Today we have a compli-

---

[1] Prager, The Early Growth and Influence of Intellectual Property, 34 Jl. Patent Office Soc. 106 (1952).

[2] Darcy v. Allein, 11 Coke 84b (K. B., 1602); The Clothworkers of Ipswich, 11 Coke 53a (K. B., 1614); Statute of Monopolies, 21 Jac. 1, Ch. 3 (1624).

cated body of law and practice that reflects the response of the legislature, the judiciary, and administrators to the many problems that have arisen.

This is not to suggest that the patent system is without defects and present problems. Like other economic and legal institutions it has many. Indeed, with the changes in research and development in recent years, the current problems faced by the Patent Office, and changes taking place in foreign countries, there are unusually strong reasons to consider what the patent system is contributing to our technical progress and how it can be made more effective. A full-scale examination of this type requires study of how technology is created and how it is applied by industry. It demands a consideration of the practices of the Patent Office and the present and future problems with which the agency is confronted. It requires examination of judicial decisions relating to patents, as well as related fields such as the antitrust law. In addition, a full-scale evaluation of the patent system demands a consideration of actual business practices relating to licensing and enforcement of patent rights.

We cannot undertake a comprehensive study of this sort in the present paper. However, we can treat briefly the basic theory of the patent system, discuss the limitations of patent rights as a mode of stimulating the creation and application of technology, and assess in a limited way the nature of patent rights of today in relation to the theory. As this last subject is a dramatic illustration of how changes have taken place over the years, it will also illustrate the growth of law and practice in this field.

⅄ The characteristic feature of the patent system is the grant of the right to exclude others from making, using, and selling the subject matter of the patented invention. There are, of course, many alternatives to a patent system. One is to let technology take its course without any government effort at all. If one should conclude that the present rate of technological change is excessive, a case can be made for moving in this direction. Few persons today, however, would accept this basic conclusion. The contributions of technology to our standard of living and to the national defense are too clear and too important for this course. A second alternative is complete socialization of research and the application of technology. This approach is equally untenable. It would involve total government intrusion into the affairs of business, not only in connection with research but also in the application of technology and, therefore, the products made by industry.

× Another, more practical, alternative to the patent system is government monetary awards for invention. Proposals for such awards can be traced back many years. Indeed, their use has frequently been closely associated with the patent system itself. One of the proposals made at the Constitutional Convention would have authorized the Congress to encourage invention by "premiums and provisions."[3] This language would permit both monetary awards and patent rights. The more narrow authorization now in the Constitution extends only to the grant of "exclusive rights" for "limited times." Through the years, Congress has used other constitutional powers to provide direct monetary awards and grants to stimulate invention. In some instances special patent rights have been authorized with provisions giving them the effect of a monetary award.[4] And since World War II we have had a statutory award system in the field of atomic energy.[5]

An important monetary award system now exists with respect to governmental use of patented inventions. A 1910 statute, amended in 1918, provides that a patent owner can secure a judgment in the Court of Claims for his "reasonable and entire" compensation for the use of a patented invention by or for the government.[6]

Award systems involve serious administrative difficulties. Some award-making authority must consider the usually complicated scientific questions, weigh the merits of purely technical contributions vis-a-vis initiative and perseverance in applying technology, and otherwise assess the case for an award. Then an amount to be paid out of the public purse must be ascertained. These problems, together with the departure of any award system from the principles of private competitive enterprise, have led to rejection of awards as the general mechanism to stimulate technical advance.[7]

---

[3] Federico, The Constitutional Provision, *18 Jl. Patent Office Soc.* 55 (July, 1936).

[4] *Private Law 1008,* 64 Stat. A 243 (1950) and *Radio Position Finding Corp.* v. *Bendix Corporation,* 205 Fed. Supp. 850 (1962).

[5] *Atomic Energy Act of 1954,* Chapter 13.

[6] *28 U.S.C. 1948.*

[7] C. Kaysen and D. F. Turner, *Antitrust Policy* (Cambridge: Harvard University Press, 1959), p. 162. But see Dupie and Lakoff, *Science and the Nation, Policy and Politics* (1962), p. 42.

Finally, we now have the de facto socialization of a substantial segment of formal research through government financing. There has been much controversy as to the proper disposition of patent rights resulting from this research. Whatever is done, government financed research stands as a sharp (but by no means recent) departure from reliance on the patent system as the source of initiative and investment in the research.[8]

A word of caution must be expressed in connection with government-financed research. Published dollar figures indicate that some 60–70 percent of all research in the United States is government financed.[9] Definitional problems require qualifications in any figure of this sort. The figure makes no attempt to—and cannot—reflect the extent to which research has a "fall out" applicable to civilian technology, or items such as the product-improvement efforts of small and medium sized business that are not reflected in figures in formal research.

Data on agricultural research bring out the point. Research in this field has long been a matter of government concern. The Department of Agriculture and the various states have expended large sums in such research. And there can be no question as to the extent technology has transformed agriculture. Hybrid corn alone has been credited with increasing the value of farm production by $800 million in 1962. Yet in this very important field of activity, the number of persons employed in research by industry in 1962 was about three times the number employed by the Department of Agriculture and about three times the number employed by the various states.[10] We could cite many other illustrations showing the fallacy of giving undue weight to the percentage figures on government-financed research.

---

[8] Classic examples of government-financed research are the $30,000 provided by the Congress in 1843 to Samuel B. Morse for his Washington-Baltimore telegraph experiment and the $5,000 voted to Samuel P. Langley for his aeronautical experiments. The latter is an especially interesting illustration because Langley was widely regarded as the leading experimenter in the quest for a flying machine but the first operable machine came from the efforts of the Wright brothers who were rated as having little chance of success.

[9] *Hearings,* Government and Science, Committee on Science and Astronautics, House of Representatives, October 16, 1963, p. 73; and Klaw, The Nationalization of U.S. Science, *Fortune,* September, 1964, p. 158.

[10] *Hearings,* The Role and Effect of Technology in the Nation's Economy, Select Committee on Small Business, United States Senate, June 5, 1963, p. 139.

Hybrid corn illustrates the importance of distinguishing between government-financed research and the application of technology in the civilian domain. By about 1917, the studies of E. M. East at the Connecticut Agricultural Experiment Station had led to the double cross method that is the technological basis for the hybrid corn industry. Yet, over 20 years passed before hybrid seed corn was in common use.[11] There are, of course, many explanations for this prolonged delay—but no explanation can avoid the practical fact that this exceedingly important advance was only slowly transferred from the domain of science to the field of practical usefulness.

For the most part, government-financed research has been in defense, space and other fields where applications to civilian technology are "fall out" and not the objective. There are, however, some instances where the capacities of private concerns are insufficient to undertake necessary research projects. The supersonic transport design is a good example.[12] In some other fields the Congress has allocated funds in the belief that the prospective benefits warrant investment of public money over and above investments of industry. The best example is the National Institute of Health's research program.[13] The fact remains, however, that to date the patent system has been generally relied upon to bring about the requisite research activity by industry. There appears to be little chance of a basic change in this reliance in the immediate future. It follows that the patent system warrants consideration in any program devoted to technical change and the role of government.

⅄ The patent system can be viewed as a way of converting invention to a "property" interest. In the patent application and issuance proceedings, the inventor or his assignee is required to define what the invention is. The end result—the patent document—is supposed to (and ordinarily does) delineate what is within and what is without the rights conveyed. So long as any significant rights are granted in the field of inventions, there must be a definitional

---

[11] H. K. Hayes, *A Professor's Story of Hybrid Corn* (Minneapolis: Burgess Publishing Co., 1963), pp. 6, 36; Crabb, *The Hybrid-Corn Makers: Prophets of Plenty* (New Brunswick: Rutgers University Press, 1947), p. 84; and *Double-Cross Hybrid Corn* (Circular 198, Connecticut Agricultural Experiment Station, June, 1956).

[12] *Wall Street Jl.*, May 25, 1964, p. 7. And editorial, *New York Times*, February 4, 1964, p. 32.

[13] *Health Research and Training*, House Report No. 321, April 28, 1961.

document of this sort. The process of evolving the document is not and cannot be simple. It entails utilization of scarce manpower having the scientific ability to comprehend the invention and the linguistic and legal skills to prepare and assess the definitional document itself. We need ways to streamline the process, to avoid making expensive determinations of "invention" or other questions that are not essential, and in other respects to do this job more effectively than it is now being done. The fact remains, however, that this is a most basic and most important procedure.

⊬ One result of converting the invention to a document of definition is that it provides the basis for granting rights and a "property" that can be transferred or licensed. The right to transfer property generally for a consideration is an essential attribute of the private property system. It is equally essential in the specific field of patent rights.

⊬ The importance of a document defining the patent right is brought out by experience in the field of confidential disclosure of ideas to business concerns. Such disclosures are often made without any definition of what is within and what is without the disclosure. The courts, seeking equitable judgments in cases with which they have been confronted, have been compelled to make after the fact determinations of the subject matter for which there is an obligation to pay. The results have been so unsatisfactory to business concerns that they usually insist upon protective agreements before receiving disclosures. Usually such agreements recite that there is no obligation to make compensation except to the extent that the person involved protects himself through patent rights.

⊦ A second and very important result of defining the patent right is that the definition advises competitors of what is inside and what is outside the scope of the right. As an experienced judge observed:[14]

⊬ The patent system encourages invention, not only in that it rewards the inventor with a patent, but it spurs the competitors to put forth their mightiest effort to produce a product as good, yet different from the patentee's. . . . It must be admitted that in an effort to avoid infringement of a patent, as much skill is often displayed as is shown in the conception or development of the invention itself. There is, however, nothing objectionable in this. In fact, it is thus that the patent system is

---

[14] Evans, J., in *James P. Marsh Corp.* v. *United States Gauge Co.*, 129 F (2d) 161, 165 (1942).

working at its best. For it is then that we have competition between a holder of a legal monopoly and his competitors. It illustrates how the legal monopoly evidenced by a patent excites the competitors to their best to meet or excel the product covered by the existing patent. Competition among industrial rivals and inventors is thus incited.

A second important aspect of the patent system is that it encourages disclosure of technical advances and discourages secrecy. To the extent scientific information is kept secret, there is a strong retarding factor in the advance of technology. The free flow of both basic and applied scientific knowledge is absolutely essential to the most rapid rate of progress and maximum utilization of our scientific resources. Of course, many scientists seek to gain professional recognition by publication and essentially all scientists feel thwarted and unhappy if their right to speak out is suppressed; but neither of these considerations alters the loss to the entrepreneur who invests in research and development when unrestrained appropriation of the published information is possible. In the absence of patents, he must insist upon secrecy or give the information to competitors to use. Nor does it answer the point to state that important technical advances become public information sooner or later in any event. The need is for the most prompt and uninhibited disclosure possible. If the inventor or his assignee can obtain tolerable protection by filing a patent application (before or within some defined time in relation to the publication), business enterprise can afford to invest in research and at the same time permit disclosure of the results.

There are many fields where trade secrets are now the practical substitute for or alternative to patent protection. One outstanding example is hybrid seed corn production. The intensive efforts of the producers were and are based on "closed" hybrids made from parents that are carefully maintained secrets. Today the proportion of "closed" hybrid seed sold in the major corn producing states is above 90 percent.[15]

Industry resorts to secrets as a mode of protection in many other fields. Secret microorganism cultures for antibiotic production are carefully guarded by many pharmaceutical producers. Indeed, the theft of such secret organisms on an international scale has been a

---

[15] Hayes, *op. cit.* supra note 11, p. 179.

matter of major attention in recent years.[16] The specific ingredients
of plastics and alloy compositions are usually maintained in secrecy.
Photographic emulsion manufacture rests on carefully guarded
secret techniques. To the extent secrets such as these are relied upon
and maintained, the patent system has failed and the interchange of
scientific information is retarded.

Third, the patent system spreads decision-making in research and
in the application of technology. This is all-important. One of the
clear lessons of history is that the "experts" in both industry and
Government are likely to miss important technical leads, to assume
that some particular technical approach is the only practical approach, and to resist fresh thoughts. With surprising frequency it is
the uninhibited "outsider" who comes forth with the key concept
that breaks a technical bottleneck. This applies both on the level of
research and on the level of application of technology. The answer to
this problem does not reside in uninformed and unguided financial
or other encouragement to the "outsider." In most instances the
"experts" are correct and the wild schemes do not economically
justify pursuit. Rather, the answer resides in the presence of many
"customers" for each fresh idea, and a strong incentive on the part of
each to bring the idea to practical and successful application. There
is much to be said for spreading decision making in the economy
generally. This is, indeed, an important aspect of the free enterprise
system. In the field of research and the application of technology—
where a strong element of unpredictability is always present—this
consideration is especially important. Patent rights can afford some
assurance to the "outsider" and those who invest in him that they
will reap a financial return commensurate with their success and will
not see such success dissipated by undue copying by the existing
industry.

The need for encouraging the sources of fresh technical thoughts
can hardly be exaggerated. There are countless examples where the
established concerns have missed technical opportunities. Sir Alex-
ander Fleming had determined the principal properties of penicillin
in 1929. The information was available to the world from that date
on. Fleming followed the theory that publication and public dedica-
tion of discoveries was necessarily good. Some limited efforts to

[16] Wolk, Some Legal Aspects of Industrial Espionage, 9 *The Practical Lawyer*
87 (1963); F.D.C. Reports, July 13, 1964, pp. 4–9.

pursue his lead did occur. But no "promoter" appeared to push this important invention. As a consequence, penicillin was not pursued by anyone in a spirit of private incentive, the resources necessary for its perfection were not committed for some years, and almost fifteen years passed before the product became available for human use.[17]

Many illustrations show the importance of spreading the decision making process with respect to new ideas. The dramatic breakthrough drug in the tranquilizer field is chlorpromazine. That drug was first made in France by Rhone-Poulenc, a large pharmaceutical house there. It was a chemical compound in the general class known as phenothiazines. These compounds—including close chemical cousins of chlorpromazine—had been the subject of detailed investigation as insecticides, antihistamines, anthelmintics, and as possible antimalarial compounds. Rhone-Poulenc pursued the compound for a different reason—its ability to potentiate or increase the action of barbiturate drugs. Efforts were made to license manufacture and sale of chlorpromazine in the United States. A number of pharmaceutical houses refused to buy. Their decisions rested at least in part on the limited patent prospects resulting from the prior disclosures of almost the same chemical compound. Finally, one of the smaller United States concerns took a license. The subsequent work of this concern, coupled with that of Rhone-Poulenc, led to discovery of the tranquilizer properties of the drug. The drug opened a whole new field of drug therapy for mental illness. It broke the trend of increased mental hospital population and has been of incalculable benefit. This case, incidentally, illustrates unpredictable good fortune giving rise to unusual success. But whether the result of long-shot prediction or of happenstance, chlorpromazine shows the need to spread decision-making on technical matters.

The wire type photoflash lamp is another illustration. This lamp was developed in 1935 by engineers at N. V. Philips in the Netherlands. Nonexclusive licenses were offered to General Electric and Westinghouse, each of which refused. A small lamp concern (one of a number of General Electric "B" licensees with a limited quota of incandescent lamps) accepted the Philips terms. The concern, Wabash Appliance Corporation, produced the lamp very success-

---

[17] Jewkes, Sawers, and Stillerman, *The Sources of Invention* (New York: St. Martin's Press, 1958), pp. 23–4 and 338–9.

fully.[18] By 1938 Wabash sales exceeded those of G. E.[19] Wabash later unsuccessfully brought patent infringement proceedings against General Electric when the latter met the competition by a modification of its prior lamp.[20]

The spread of decision making in relation to research and new products is especially important in connection with entry into an industry by "outsiders." The nearly universal conclusion of students of technical progress has been that the products and processes of major significance tend to originate outside an industry. Synthetic fibers and synthetic finishes have been listed as the major advances in the textile industry in about the last 30 years. Both originated outside the industry.[21] In machine tools the major technical developments since about World War I are carbide tools and numerical controls. The former came from the Krupp works in Germany. The latter was the result of Air Force sponsored research at MIT.[22] Photographic methods of document copying were known long before the advent of the office copying machine. But it was a concern entirely outside the photographic industry that marketed the first office copying machine. And the latest turnover in this industry has been the result of the Xerox machine which was perfected and marketed by a concern that had not previously participated in the office copying machine industry. The electric typewriter was marketed first by IBM, not an existing typewriter manufacturer.

An analyst of technology in the electrical industry has noted that:[23]

> . . . It cannot be only chance that the Western Union interests underestimated the telephone, that the Telephone Company was slow to appreciate the possibilities of radio, that it remained for newcomers to bring out the inexpensive table model radio receiver, the small concerns did much of the pioneer work in fluorescent lighting, and that one small concern made the first F.M. transmitters while a local network was the first commercial enterprise to install them.

---

[18] Bright, *The Electric-Lamp Industry* (1949), pp. 340–1.

[19] *Wabash Appliance Co.* v. *General Electric Co.*, 187 F(2d) 577 (1951), Exhibit 28–13.

[20] *Wabash Appliance Co.* v. *General Electric Co.*, 187 F(2d) 577 (1951).

[21] *Hearings*, The Role and Effect of Technology in the Nation's Economy, Select Subcommittee on Small Business, U.S. Senate, May 20, 1963, p. 105.

[22] *Ibid.*

[23] Kottke, *Electrical Technology and the Public Interest* (1944), p. 127.

We could go on endlessly with illustrations of this sort—all showing that existing industry leaders cannot be relied upon to pursue all of the important new ideas. There must, accordingly, be some strong incentive for the smaller concerns and newcomers. Patents play an important role in providing such incentives.

Government has been equally unable to identify the most promising new techniques. In government, as in business, there are always strong factors working against any change. These often justify discarding a new approach, but occasionally they lead to rejection of a new technique that should be pursued. An example is the turbo-jet airplane. The principles of the turbo-jet plane were known long before World War II. At least one industrial concern in the United States had investigated the engine and had concluded that it was not feasible at the time. The United States Government followed a similar view. There was ample justification for this attitude, for the engine required high temperature high strength materials for efficient operation. These materials were not available until the World War II period. But the negative factors were overemphasized. This was belatedly discovered when word was received of the success of Commander Whittle in Great Britain and the activity of the Germans. The result was that our military relied upon piston type engines virtually throughout the war and the United States was far behind on this key development. At one time the Germans could have acquired control of the skies using available jet engines in interceptor aircraft. They failed only because Adolph Hitler foolishly insisted that the engines be placed in bombers.[24]

Small concerns and newcomers to an industry play a particularly important role as a source of new techniques and new products. They have a smaller vested interest than the larger concerns in the existing technology. They usually have a stronger desire to grow in size. But such concerns suffer from lack of established reputation, trade connections, sales facilities, and production plant. With a new product or process, the smaller concern or the newcomer can offset these disadvantages in considerable measure. But if competitors can copy the process or product once it proves successful, the small concern or newcomer may lose the advantage of its innovative efforts. This is why small businessmen and their financial supporters have had a warm regard for the patent system.

[24] Schlaifer, *Development of Aircraft Engines* (1950), pp. 321–508.

Polaroid Corporation is an example of a small concern, at least relatively speaking, that pioneered a new technique in reliance upon patent rights. Edwin H. Land of Polaroid has said:[25]

. . . It is impossible—without the protection of patents—for a new company working on a major advance in science or technology to (1) be properly financed; (2) go through the extremely difficult periods of study, invention, development, engineering, and production; or (3) afford to advertise and distribute its products and services.

Polaroid was initially financed in reliance upon the patents to the light polarizer inventions of Dr. Land. It entered the photographic industry in 1948 with heavy reliance on the prospective patent rights to the "Land" camera and film.[26]

There is a great need to assure that decision-making is sufficiently spread to assure fair consideration of offbeat ideas. But it is as undesirable to pursue all such ideas as it is to pursue none. The commitment of Dr. Ivy to Krebiozen is ample indication that the proponents of the new ideas can be wrong too.[27] There must be a measure of restraint as to the fresh ideas as well as in other fields. Patent rights provide an incentive, coupled with a restraint. Unless the investor perceives a reasonable prospect of success, the investment will not be made. This is the same selection process that applies to business investments generally and forms a fundamental aspect of a free enterprise economy.

Fourth, an effective patent system applies an essential spur to research and the application of technology by every concern. There are important justifications for a go-slow policy by business enterprise in utilizing a new technology. To be sure, the risks are small and there is little reason to pause when the matter is one of a trivial variation in the form of an automobile tail fin, the contours of a refrigerator, or the positions of the knobs of a radio receiver. But where a substantial change from the old technology is involved, a different situation prevails. The risks of failure are great, the economic life of plant and production equipment may be cut short, new inventory and supply problems are created, engineering, service and

---

[25] Thinking Ahead: Patents and New Enterprise, 37 *Harv. Bus. Rev.* 7, 9 (1959).

[26] *Hearings*, American Patent System, Subcommittee on Patents, Trademarks, and Copyrights, U.S. Senate, October, 1955, p. 266.

[27] What Ever Happened to Dr. Ivy?, *Life*, October 9, 1964, p. 110.

other personnel must master the new process or product, sales forces require new training, and users must be educated as to the advantages and disadvantages of the new process or product. Of course these problems are not insurmountable. But they do create a barrier to change that must be overcome. These short run obstacles may outweigh the long term prospective advantages of a promising new technology in the absence of additional forces that dictate adoption of the new approach.

When patents afford some exclusive rights to the new technique, business cannot afford to be too conservative in research for and the application of the change. An existing concern may be entirely happy with the present state of affairs. But if competitors threaten to pursue an important new technology and enjoy both the benefits of being "first in" and some opportunity to exclude the second-comer, the existing concern must pursue technical advance if it is to survive.

It should be noted that the barrier to the adoption of a new technology may exist even though the required scientific information is available and open for use by all. This is why the policy of simply publishing scientific information—such as was followed by Fleming with penicillin—may in fact be the most undesirable policy from the standpoint of bringing the technology to practical use.

These aspects of the patent system may be viewed in terms of competition. Properly operating, the patent system increases the extent that business enterprise competes in research and competes in applying each new technology. Such competition is in addition to competition in price, production, and other effort. To be sure, one can characterize patents as "monopolies." This term continues to arise in legal decisions and economic commentary. But it was pointed out at least by the time of Daniel Webster that there is nothing more "monopolistic" in the ownership of a patent than in the ownership of a house, a strategically located plot of land, a source of water power, or a mine. In each instance the "property" right is the medium by which a free enterprise economy stimulates the creation and effective use of the property and hence competitive effort.

It is most significant that the instances of most rapid technological advance in industry have taken place in the presence of vigorous and unrelenting research and new product or process competition. The German chemical industry reached its advanced state by about 1900 as the consequence of the dye industry technical competition that took place following the German patent law of 1876.[28] The rapid development of the electrical power industry in this country at approximately the same time was the consequence of intense competition between competing entrepreneurs. These included Thomas Edison, whose mistaken notions as to alternating current would have retarded progress a great deal more if his competitors had not been on the scene.[29] Burton was denied an opportunity to try his thermal cracking ideas by the Standard Oil of New Jersey management. But after the 1911 antitrust decree made Standard of Indiana an independent concern, he was authorized to proceed. Intensive cracking process development competition ensued. In the subsequent years the research activity stimulated by Burton's work not only led to a more efficient utilization of crude oil in the production of gasoline but in addition led to the creation of the petrochemicals industry.[30] The drug industry of the past 20 years abounds in illustrations of successive new drugs and vast and sharp shifts in company market position resulting from vigorous research and new product competition.[31] These and many other illustrations may be cited to show that when the necessary basic science foundation is present, a competitive industry exists, and rights are available for the protection of discoveries, business enterprise has a truly remarkable ability to move forward in technical matters.

The converse of this observation is often overlooked. Technical indolence by private enterprise is an indication of monopoly. The monopolist can charge a monopolistic price in terms of stand-pat technology, just as much as in connection with prices. As Judge Wyzanski has observed:[32] ". . . Some truth lurks in the cynical remark that not high profits but a quiet life is the chief reward of monopoly power. . . ." The wisdom of this observation is borne out by the antitrust cases that have condemned efforts by business concerns to foreclose the competition of new products and processes.[33]

[28] J. J. Beer, The Emergence of the German Dye Industry (Urbana, Ill.: University of Illinois Press, 1959), pp. 105–110.

[29] Harold Clarence Passer, The Electrical Manufacturers (Cambridge: Harvard University Press, 1953), pp. 164–175.

[30] J. L. Enos, Petroleum Progress and Profits (Cambridge, Mass., M.I.T. Press, 1962), pp. 20–22.

[31] Hearings on H.R. 6245, May 1962, Committee on the Judiciary, House of Representatives, pp. 563–607.

[32] U.S. v. United Shoe Machinery Corp., 110 Fed. Supp. 295, 347 (1953).

[33] Kobe, Inc. v. Dempsey Pump Co., 198 F(2d) 416 (1952) and U.S. v. General Electric Co., 82 Fed. Supp. 753 (1949).

With an effective patent system and effective antitrust law enforcement, monopoly power of this sort should be rare.

There is an important limitation inherent in the patent system. So long as the totality of patent rights owned by each concern does not foreclose competition by creative competitors, all concerns must compete in technical matters as well as price, production, and other aspects of business. But if a concern owns a single patent or a group of patents that foreclose competition, it may follow an indolent policy towards further research and technical change. In short, patent rights that are too extensive may defeat the very purpose of the patent system.

This undesirable condition can exist for either of two reasons. One is through the aggregation of a large number of patents in the hands of one owner or a group of cooperating owners. The other is by the issuance of a single patent that is unduly broad in scope. The first problem is now minimized through application of the antitrust laws. The second is largely avoided by developments through the years in the law and practice relating to patents. In each instance we have clear examples of how legal doctrine has grown in response to apparent need.

Until about 1890, the date of the Sherman Act, there were very few combinations of patent owners with aggregate rights sufficient to foreclose substantial competition. Indeed, it was not combinations of businessmen to accumulate patents that motivated the Act, but rather combinations of competitors unrelated to patents. Nevertheless, in *Pope* v. *Gormully*,[34] decided shortly after the Sherman Act, the court refused relief on the equitable ground that the combination of patent owners involved was against the public interest. The case did not involve any issues as to the Sherman Act and thus stands as a classic illustration of how enforcement of the patent law may lead to results similar to those associated with Sherman Act enforcement. Subsequent decisions based on the Sherman Act have held that combinations of patent owners to foreclose or control competition are illegal.[35]

Acquisition of patents through purchase and for the purpose of

---

[34] *Pope* v. *Gormully*, 144 U.S. 224 (1892).

[35] *Hartford-Empire Co.* v. *U.S.* 323 U.S. 386 (1945); *Blount* v. *Yale and Towne Mfg. Co.*, 166 Fed. 555 (1909); *U.S.* v. *New Departure Mfg. Co.*, 204 Fed. 107 (1913); and *U.S.* v. *General Instrument Corp.*, 87 Fed. Supp. 157 (1949).

monopolization by patent accumulation has similarly been held illegal under the Sherman Act.[36] In recent years a more strict standard of legality has become applicable to patent acquisitions by reason of the 1950 amendment to Section 7 of the Clayton Act.[37] This amendment forbids certain acquisitions of all or any part of the "assets" of a corporation—a term that includes the acquisition of patent rights.[38] As Carl Kaysen has pointed out, there are limitations on the strictness with which Section 7 should be applied.[39] But whatever the outcome of current trends towards very strict Section 7 enforcement, it is now clear that patent accumulation through purchase is subject to antitrust law limitations that largely close off this route to an undue accumulation of patent rights.

There remains, of course, the possibility of a single company acquiring an unduly broad collection of patent rights by making a vast number of important inventions itself. An illustration of this is found in exhibit 388 in the Hartford-Empire case. There an executive of Hartford-Empire listed some of the reasons for taking out patents. He named the three main purposes as:[40]

(*a*) To cover the actual machines which we are putting out and prevent duplication of them.

(*b*) To block the development of machines which might be constructed by others for the same purposes as our machines, using alternative means.

(*c*) To secure patents on possible improvements of competing machines, so as to "fence in" those and prevent their reaching an improved stage.

The second and third purposes are clearly antisocial in terms of technical advance. The memorandum, incidentally, was one of the main items of evidence relied upon by the Government in showing Hartford's anticompetitive intent and purpose.

As a practical matter it is now exceedingly difficult for any single concern to finance research on the scale required to accumulate such a large number of patents as to foreclose effective research and new

---

[36] *Kobe* v. *Dempsey Pump Co.*, supra note 33.

[37] 64 Stat. 1125.

[38] *U.S.* v. *Lever Brothers Co.*, 216 Fed. Supp. 901 (1962).

[39] C. Kaysen, The New Competition and the Old Regulation (Chap. 10, this volume).

[40] *U.S.* v. *Hartford-Empire Company*, 46 Fed. Supp. 541 (1942).

product competition by competitors. This has, to be sure, occurred in some instances where monopoly power has existed in a significant market and business policies have thwarted the activities of competitors. One such instance is the United Shoe Machinery Corp., which was held by Judge Wyzanski to have violated Section 2 of the Sherman Act by reason of its overall business activity.[41] Another instance is the General Electric Company in the field of lamps. Here, Judge Forman held that both Section 1 and Section 2 of the Sherman Act were violated.[42] Among the activities emphasized by the Government and by Judge Forman were patent licensing practices that stifled the patent incentives otherwise applicable to the other companies in the field.

Additionally, there have been instances where unusually creative research and marketing activity has enabled business concerns to manufacture and sell specific products under patent protection that precludes competitors from making those particular products. The history of moistureproof cellophane is an illustration. DuPont, the pioneer in the field, obtained a broad product patent to moistureproof cellophane and for a substantial period cellophane manufacture was confined to DuPont and its licensee. But when the government accused the company of monopolizing the cellophane market in violation of Section 2 of the Sherman Act, Judge Leahy found that the relevant market was not cellophane, but rather was all flexible packaging materials. A majority of the Supreme Court agreed with this conclusion. The point is that while DuPont might have enjoyed patent rights to moistureproof cellophane it was always subject to the competition of other flexible packaging materials that were not subject to its control. In the relevant market—flexible packaging materials—DuPont did not have the power to fix prices and exclude competitors as necessary for a finding of monopoly power.[43] This illustration is especially significant because the moistureproof cellophane patent was unusually broad.

A number of factors combine to make patent rights as broad as the cellophane patent exceedingly unusual. These include the Patent Office practices in granting patents, the legal decisions on patent construction, the effects of antitrust law and other legal doctrines on

41 U.S. v. United Shoe Machinery Corp., supra note 32.
42 U.S. v. General Electric Company, supra note 33.
43 U.S. v. E. I. DuPont, 118 Fed. Supp. 41 (1953), aff'd. at 351 U.S. 377 (1956).

the permitted use of patent rights, and the varying business practices associated with licensing and enforcing patents. Let us briefly consider these factors, and particularly the way they have developed over the years.

Patent Office administration is important because it determines the character of the patent document as issued, and hence the defined scope of the patent rights. Indeed, attention in the Patent Office is largely directed to defining what, if anything, is patentable subject matter. Usually the applicant seeks broad patent rights as represented by broad claims, the patent examiner locates pertinent prior art and insists that the broad claims sought are not patentable, and the finally issued patent has more narrow claims than those originally sought. The process is tedious, complex, and expensive. But in the end it usually serves to limit the scope of the patent rights and does so in a way that indicates clearly the subject matter not covered by the patent. Court proceedings are ordinarily not necessary. A strong case can be made that in this respect the Patent Office has been highly successful.

The present highly sophisticated Patent Office practice with respect to claims is an excellent example of how practice has developed to meet need. Even now, the patent statutes relating to claims are quite broad and general. Prior to 1952, the statutes did little more than indicate that the patent applicant shall "particularly point out and distinctly claim" his invention.[44] After the Civil War, and especially after about 1900, the Patent Office became progressively more stringent in its requirements as to the content and form of claims, the emphasis always being on requiring a more precise definition of what is within and what is without the patent subject matter. While court decisions have had a part in this history,[45] the credit must largely go to step-by-step improvements brought about by the Patent Office administrations.

In assessing the place of the Patent Office in bringing about an effective definition of patent subject matter, consideration should be given to the condition that existed in the 42 year period from 1793 to 1836. During this time a simple registration system was used in this country. The system led to an intolerable number of invalid, con-

---

44 35 U.S.C. 112 (present law); Section 4888 R.S. (prior law).
45 General Electric Co. v. Jewel Incandescent Lamp Co., 326 U.S. 242 (1945).

flicting, and even fraudulent patents. The examination system was accordingly restored and the present Patent Office established.[46] Despite the many practical problems now associated with Patent Office operations, there is a consensus that a patent examining system is highly desirable and probably essential.

The legal decisions construing patents have a pronounced effect on the scope of patent rights. In the last analysis, the decisive question is what a court will hold a patent to cover. The court decisions have been more responsive to "equities" than the Patent Office, and have given greater emphasis to the contribution to the art than patent law technicalities. They nevertheless have almost uniformly followed some basic principles of patent construction. The first is that a patent cannot encompass what is "prior art."[47] Second, the courts have adhered strictly to the principle that a patent cannot be construed to cover what is literally within the claims as originally sought but is outside the literal scope of the claims as issued.[48] Another rule, less strictly applied, is that a patent cannot cover what it does not expressly claim.[49]

Antitrust law and other legal doctrines impose limitations on the economic scope of patent rights. The outstanding development is the patent "misuse" doctrine set forth in a series of court decisions since about 1930.[50] These were the result of judicial irritation with the use of patents for tying purposes. Where such "misuse" exists, the courts have refused all relief for patent infringement. The anti-trust laws have had similar effects in limiting the extent patent owners can use patent licensing provisions to control competition.[51]

Business practices often greatly limit the practical scope of patent rights. The most dramatic example is the case where a difference exists between what a patent covers and what the patent owner markets. In one classic case the patent was directed to a home heating system including thermostat, stoker, and hold-fire thermostat. The patent owner sold only the hold-fire thermostat. Using rather conceptual reasoning that the thermostat, per se, was not pat-

---

[46] 1836 Report of Ruggles Committee, *18 Jl. Patent Office Soc., 853* (1936).
[47] *Union Carbide* v. *Graver Tank*, 196 F(2d) 103 (1952).
[48] *Exhibit Supply Co.* v. *Ace Patents Corp.*, 315 U.S. 126 (1942).
[49] *McClain* v. *Ortmayer*, 141 U.S. 419, 423–4 (1891).
[50] *Morton Salt Co.* v. *Suppiger*, 314 U.S. 488 (1942).
[51] *Standard Sanitary Mfg. Co.* v. *U.S.*, 226 U.S. 20 (1912).

ented, the Supreme Court held that the patent "misuse" doctrine precluded patent infringement relief and, additionally, sustained a counterclaim for treble damages under the antitrust laws.[52] Another classic example is that of D.D.T. This insecticide is perhaps the most important single invention of the last 25 years, at least as measured in human terms. But the active compound is an old chemical compound and as such was not patentable. In consequence, patent rights were limited to the process of using the product and to particular formulations of the active compound.[53] The process was employed only by the ultimate user of the product, and the claims to formulations were easily evaded. The patent value was accordingly limited by the business facts, together with the effects of patent law doctrine.

This is not the place for an extended discussion of the principles of patent construction and the practical and legal limitations on patent rights. A few observations based on general experience will have to suffice. First, patent rights almost never confer substantial monopoly in the trade monopoly sense. To be sure, there were the Hall and Bradley patents in the aluminum industry,[54] the Bell and Berliner patents to the telephone,[55] the Coolidge and Langmuir patents to the incandescent lamp,[56] and the Drew patent to pressure sensitive cellophane tape.[57] But these are the very rare exceptions, and they are becoming even more rare. The vast majority of patents extend only to rather specific technical contributions which are subject to alternatives and leave the patent owner with significant market competition that limits the price that can be charged and compels him to maintain his own pace of technical advance.

Many illustrations can be cited of patent rights operating in an environment of practical and effective alternatives. One is the cellophane patent, discussed above. Another is the Ray-O-Vac flashlight cell—which was little more than the prior art flashlight cell encased in a steel jacket.[58] Ray-O-Vac had hit upon a technique that the

[52] *Mercoid Corp.* v. *Mid-Continent Inv. Co.,* 320 U.S. 661 (1944) and *Mercoid Corp.* v. *Minneapolis-Honeywell Regulator Co.,* 320 U.S. 680 (1944).

[53] *Ex parte Muller,* 81 U.S.P.Q. 261 (1947).

[54] *U.S.* v. *Aluminum Co. of America,* 44 Fed. Supp. 97, 111 (1941).

[55] *U.S.* v. *American Bell Telephone Co.,* 167 U.S. 224 (1897).

[56] *U.S.* v. *General Electric Co.,* supra note 33.

[57] *Minnesota Mining & Mfg. Co.* v. *International Plastic Corporation,* 159 F(2d) 544 (1947).

[58] *Goodyear Tire and Rubber* v. *Ray-O-Vac,* 321 U.S. 275 (1944).

workers in the field had evidently overlooked or discounted. The company exploited the product and in the process increased its market position and forced the competitors to market improved products of their own. Despite favorable judicial decisions on the patent, Ray-O-Vac could not prevent the marketing of equally good or superior cells. In industries such as the radio industry today, the worth of even the most important patents is limited by the cost of resort to equally good but slightly more expensive alternative circuitry or technique. Chemical industry, especially drugs, provides even more dramatic examples of narrow patent rights. The chlorpromazine patent, directed to the pioneering tranquilizer drug, is confined to a few chemical compounds.[59] Many related compounds not covered by the patent are useful tranquilizers, with both advantages and disadvantages in relation to chlorpromazine. The patent to the most important corticosteroids (used in the treatment of arthritis and inflammatory conditions) covers only two chemical compounds and their salts.[60] Many other corticosteroids outside the scope of this patent are being marketed, again with both advantages and disadvantages in relation to the compounds of the patent.

Usually the significance of even a very important patent—no matter how jealously enforced—is a modest cost of "designing around" the patented subject matter. The second-comer can usually devise its own competing product or process outside the scope of the patent. Of course this takes a measure of skill, some investment, and some risk-taking. But the skill, investment, and risk are ordinarily far less than those of the pioneering patent owner. It is surprising how often the result is a decidedly better product or process, based on general lessons derived from the pioneer but not patented or patentable. The process may be viewed as one in which the second-comer is required to finance its own technology, or pay royalties to the pioneer. Such patent rights serve to reward the pioneering concern that makes the major investments and takes the principal risks. But they do not prevent others from following the lead.

Finally, an important analogy should be considered. Success in business generally creates a market position and market power. In theory, and sometimes in actual fact, the result is monopoly power or an approach to monopoly power. Substantial market power, unre-

[59] Patent 2,645,640.
[60] Patent 3,134,718.

lated to patents, is common. It exists, for example, in concentrated industries such as the automobile industry. Actual monopoly of limited geographical scope is very common. Examples include the theatre in a one-theatre town,[61] the only building in a city favorably situated for produce marketing operations,[62] a vital railroad terminal facility,[63] the only cement mill within economical shipping distance of a customer, and the only television station in an area where interference problems make only one channel available. There are a few instances of nationwide monopoly of an important product. This was once true of aluminum.[64] It has more recently been true, and may still be true, in the case of linen rugs.[65] We accept these possibilities, as we must, as the price of an economy where business effort is encouraged by the incentive of economic self-interest. The fact of actual monopoly was recognized at the time of the Sherman Act, as was the point that monopoly, per se, would not offend the Act.[66] In short, competition itself can lead to monopoly. The anti-trust laws reflect a trade-off between the encouragement of greater competitive effort and preventing the attainment and continuation of monopoly. Judicial decisions have tended to shift the trade-off in the direction of preventing monopoly. But no matter where the line is drawn, the trade-off is inescapably present because competition itself may breed monopoly.

An analogous effect occurs with patent rights. Creative effort in the field of invention may give rise to important patent rights. Vigorous commercial marketing based on the patent rights can lead to a significant business. In theory—although almost never in practice—the rights can be so important that they insulate the owner from substantial competition for the period of the patent. But if patent rights are too broad in scope, it would be theoretically possible for the patent system to defeat its own purpose. This is another way of saying that the line of trade-off between incentive to create and market inventions and competition thereafter can be

[61] *U.S.* v. *Griffith,* 334 U.S. 100 (1948).

[62] *Gamco, Inc.* v. *Providence Fruit and Produce Bld'g.,* 194 F(2d) 484 (1952).

[63] *U.S.* v. *Terminal Railroad Association of St. Louis,* 224 U.S. 383 (1912).

[64] *U.S.* v. *Aluminum Co. of America,* 44 Fed. Supp. 97 (1941).

[65] *U.S.* v. *Klearflax Linen Looms,* 63 Fed. Supp. 32 (1945).

[66] *U.S.* v. *Aluminum Co. of America,* supra note 64 at pp. 159–160.

drawn at a point that stifles future invention. As in the case of competition generally, this risk of possible monopoly is the price that must be paid to assure competition in originally creating and marketing the inventions. It should be added that with present antitrust doctrine and antitrust enforcement policy, and with present standards of patent issuance and patent enforcement, the trade-off is now at a point where the risk of undue patent rights or accumulations of patent rights is slight.

We can conclude our discussion of the role of patent rights by considering a few facts of general character touching on the chemical and drug industry:

1. In Italy, no patent rights are available for drugs and methods of making them. Patent rights are available in the field of chemicals generally. Italian industry and Italian science are highly advanced in the field of chemicals generally. In organic polymers and plastics, Italian science is especially strong.[67] It produced a Nobel prize winner in 1963. In petrochemical manufacture, Italian industry is a world leader. But in the field of drugs, Italy is the situs of "pirate" manufacture based on drugs pioneered by concerns in other countries. Not a single important new drug has emerged from the Italian industry.

2. In Germany, the dye industry was established before the First Reich and at a time when no effective patent rights were available. German copying of dye discoveries made in Great Britain and France ultimately drove manufacturers in these countries to discontinue their own new product efforts. The resulting stagnation of the dye industry in Germany led the industry to seek patent legislation soon after the First Reich. This led to the patent act of 1876. It was after this act that the German dye industry entered into its great period of new product competition that was one of the most productive periods of all time in terms of applied scientific discovery. This period of development led to the advanced state of chemical technology at the time of World War I and had an important influence on the German war potential.[68]

3. In the United States today, both drug and chemical industry is engaged in fierce competition to find and market new drug, insecticide, plastic, fiber, and other products. Competition emphasizes research and development and marketing of new products. As one commentator states "This is the famous 'test-tube competition,' or continual struggle of com-

---

[67] Natta, Precisely Constructed Polymers, *Scientific American*, August 1961, p. 33.
[68] Beer, *op. cit.* note 28, supra.

peting laboratories to find new products."[69] The emphasis on new products may be too great or too little as viewed from some economic standard, if an acceptable economic standard for such activity can be devised. But there can be little question but that this competition is desired by essentially all segments of society.

It is exceedingly doubtful that this intense research and new product competition would continue in the absence of a patent system. At least the Italian and early German dye industry experience—as well as the commentaries of industry leaders in this country[70]—so indicate. It follows that at least until some fundamental economic change occurs, patent system incentives will have an important place in stimulating business enterprise to create technology and—perhaps more important—to apply it.

[69] S. N. Whitney, *Antitrust Policies, American Experience in Twenty Industries* (New York: Twentieth Century Fund, 1958), p. 237.

[70] Edwin H. Land, supra note 25.

Congressman Daddario, from his special vantage point, analyzes legislative problems on patent policy, especially pertaining to Government sponsored research. Is it right that private parties be given patent rights when the Government has paid for the underlying research? Is it desirable that the Government should retain patent rights for itself? The author explains why his House Subcommittee favors private rights to patents, whereas the Senate Judiciary Subcommittee leans toward Government title.

EMILIO QUINCY DADDARIO has been a member of the U.S. Congress from the First Congressional District of Connecticut since 1958. He is also senior partner of the law firm of Daddario and Burns. He studied at Wesleyan University, Boston University and the University of Connecticut where he received his law degree. In Congress he is Chairman of the Special Subcommittee on Patents and Scientific Inventions.

CHAPTER 5

LEGISLATIVE PROBLEMS IN THE FIELD OF PATENTS AND PATENT POLICY

Emilio Q. Daddario

When the Congress returns to Washington in January, 1965, it will be the 175th Anniversary of one of the most important legislative acts in this Nation's proud history, the first Patent Act of 1790. It is appropriate at this point to pause momentarily and recall that the Patent Act flowed from the restraints placed on the English monarch by the Parliament. It was a statute to prevent the establishment of monopolies, *about which we hear so much in this day*, although entitled the Statute of Monopolies. The Statute, enacted in 1624, codified the English common law. The English courts had held that patents for new manufactures, granted for a limited time, were valid, because they were "for the good of the realm."

Seventeen short years after the Statute of Monopolies, Massachusetts enacted the first patent statute on this side of the Atlantic. It permitted monopolies for new inventions "that are profitable to the Countrie," and "for a short time."

One hundred and sixty-four years after the Statute of Monopolies, the Founding Fathers wrote the constitutional provision upon which our patent system is founded. Article I, Section 8, of the Constitution reads, "The Congress shall have the power to promote the progress of science and useful arts, by securing for limited times to authors and inventors the exclusive right to their respective writings and discoveries."

The Patent Act of 1790 copied and codified the British patent law.

87

It not only set forth that a "manufacture" was patentable, but added "art" and "machine," which the British courts had found to be "manufactures."

I submit that the Congress knew what it was doing; it had hundreds of years of British law before it. The colonies of Massachusetts, New Hampshire, Connecticut, Pennsylvania and Maryland had all issued patents. They were not a new and unknown quantity.

Thus we find that patents were authorized by law in England, because they were for the "good of the realm"; in the Massachusetts Bay Colony, because they were "profitable to the Countrie"; and by the Constitution, if they "promote the progress of the useful arts."

Leaders throughout our history have recognized the contribution of the patent system to technological progress and economic growth because of the incentives it provides to the inventor. President Lincoln, in presenting his second lecture on the importance to "young America" of discoveries and inventions stated, for example, that:

I have already intimated my opinion that in the world's history, certain inventions and discoveries occurred, *of peculiar value, on account of their great efficiency in facilitating all other inventions and discoveries.* Of these were the arts of writing and of printing—the discovery of America, and the introduction of Patent Laws.

These began in England in 1624; and in this country, with adoption of our Constitution. Before these, any man might instantly use what another had invented; so that the inventor had no special advantage from his own invention. The patent system changed this; secured to the inventor, for a limited time, the exclusive use of his invention; and thereby *added the fuel of interest to the fire of genius,* in the discovery and production of new and useful things.

I have quoted President Lincoln on this subject because I believe that what he said then applies with even added emphasis today.

Although I am not a patent attorney—and, unless one has just been elected, there are none in the Congress—I have become deeply immersed in certain aspects of patent law—namely, legislation directed to amend the patent provisions of the National Aeronautics and Space Act of 1958. As Chairman of the Subcommittee on Patents and Scientific Inventions of the House Committee on Science and Astronautics, I have had the opportunity to review one phase of this problem. My review has taken place while the dialogue developed over the effects which our patent policies have on research and development as we have set our sights on the achievement of important national goals.

This dialogue has developed for many valid reasons. Two are paramount; first, the tremendous sums of money which the American tapxayer is putting up to fund federal technical activities. Congress is now being asked to approve slightly more than $15 billion annually to sustain the government's interest in, and need for, research and development. Any time a federal endeavor reaches these proportions, it is bound to have serious side effects, and the danger to private patent rights which we have seen demonstrated is one of them. The second reason is that we are a nation dedicated to the basic proposition of private enterprise. We have established a system based on Anglo-American concepts of property rights, and there is no property right dearer to the hearts of our people than their ideas, and no greater interest than putting those ideas into practical use and hopefully profiting from them.

More recently, I have had the opportunity to study the impact of the patent system and the government's patent policies on, not only the successful conduct of federal research and development programs, but also on scientific and technological advancement vital to an expanding economy.

Because of growing awareness of the forceful impact of science and technology on the well-being of the nation, and also of the needs of Congress for a continuing appraisal of the problems created by science and technology, the Chairman of the House Science and Astronautics Committee, Congressman George P. Miller, created a Subcommittee on Science, Research and Development in August, 1963. I have the honor of serving as the subcommittee's chairman.

The subcommittee launched a series of general orientation hearings designed to identify and rank as many of the major scientific problem areas as possible. Witnesses and others contributing information to our inquiries were among the most outstanding and knowledgeable members of the scientific community. As a result of our general hearings, the subcommittee has acted through a variety of channels in pursuing answers to questions of immediate importance. Included are arrangements worked out with the National Academy of Sciences, the National Science Foundation, and a newly created Research Management Panel for special studies directed to managerial problems. To date, four reports have been issued by the subcommittee. Our investigations will continue in the next Congress.

Although many issues have been raised, one that demands attention at an early date is the effect of federal research and development, and the programs it sponsors, on private profit-oriented research conducted by industry. It is in this broader context of the government's role as a sponsor of research and development that the answer to the continuing issue of rights to inventions resulting from such activity may well come.

The question that has been drawn into sharp focus by the growing scale of federal investment in support of technical work is often simply stated as this:—Who shall own the rights to patentable inventions resulting from such activity? Should title to *all* vest in the federal government, or should title to *all* these inventions remain with the contractor, the federal government taking no more than a royalty-free license.

Let me suggest, however, that this issue is more apparent than real. Long study—both in relation to amendments to the Space Act and the broader topic of science, research and development—has convinced me that we simply cannot arrive at any rigid policy in one direction or the other. There must be *flexibility* in whatever over-all policy is adopted. I think that even the most extreme partisans on either side agree on this point. . . . Each concedes that a broad use of waivers would be necessary in any instance. This being the case, I would conclude that the most practical method of administering an over-all policy will involve the license approach with exceptions rather than the title approach with exceptions.

The need for a flexible patent policy, to meet the needs of the government, recognize the equities of the contractor, facilitate the commercialization of inventions and serve the public interest, was acknowledged by President Kennedy in his Memorandum on Government Patent Policy issued for the guidance of Executive Departments and Agencies on October 10, 1963. He stated, for example, that, "In view of the differing missions and statutory responsibilities of the several departments and agencies engaged in research and development, it is not feasible to have complete uniformity of practice throughout the government."

The Memorandum points out, however, that there is a need for greater consistency in agency practices in order to further the governmental and public interest in promoting the utilization of federally-financed inventions and to avoid difficulties caused by different approaches by the agencies when dealing with the same class of organizations in comparable patent situations. It also states that single presumption of ownership does not provide a satisfactory basis for government-wide policy on the allocation of rights to inventions.

In addition, the public interest in a dynamic and efficient economy requires that efforts be made to encourage the expeditious development and *civilian* use of inventions in scientific and technological fields resulting from work performed under government contracts. Both the incentives to draw forth private initiative to this end, and the need to promote healthy competition in industry must be weighed in the disposition of patent rights under government contracts.

Finally, the President's Memorandum states that the prudent administration of government research and development calls for a government-wide policy on the disposition of inventions made under government contracts reflecting common principles and objectives, to the extent consistent with the missions of the respective agencies. Such policy must recognize the need for flexibility to accommodate special situations.

Most people close to the issue generally favored the statement of policy set forth by the President. We were of the opinion that, if properly implemented, the policy would bring the disposition of rights to inventions closer to the objectives of federal research and development contracting. When the Statement was issued, I stated on the floor of the House, "It provides for a 'licensing policy with necessary exceptions' which I hope will be implemented by Executive agencies without delay."

Actual implementation of the policy has been much too slow, however. After more than a year, only two agencies have issued implementing regulations, the Department of Defense and National Aeronautics and Space Administration.

The Department of Defense largely repeated the President's words and did not provide the interpretation and guidance required in the day-by-day operation of such a complex and technical area of contracting. The current regulations actually reverse the traditional DOD position, by which the taking of title to inventions was the exception rather than the rule. Although I do not believe the Defense

Department needs, or for that matter wants, to develop a huge patent portfolio which it must then administer, the present regulations can well result in just that, and this must be carefully watched.

If the intent of the policy statement is not to be contravened in actual practice, it will be necessary for the Department of Defense to issue additional interpretive bulletins for the guidance of individual contracting officers. Experience has proven that whenever contracting officers are given the responsibility of making specific determinations by the application of fairly loose guidelines, they lean towards acquiring as much as the guidelines can be said to permit, in order to avoid possible criticism of not fully protecting the government's interest. This tendency is particularly aggravated where speed in placing a research and development contract is important.

The National Aeronautics and Space Administration (NASA) issued new Patent Waiver regulations, in accordance with the President's Policy, which were effective September 28. Although I have not had the opportunity to study these in detail, it is my understanding that they provide for three separate opportunities to obtain a waiver,—at the time of contracting—after contract execution but prior to invention reporting—and after the invention has been reported. As you know, NASA is required by Sec. 305 of the Space Act to take title to inventions *but* may waive such rights if the Administrator determines that the interests of the United States will be served thereby.

It was not intended that the Statement of Policy was to be the final word, or could not be modified. This is why it was issued as a "memorandum" rather than an Executive Order. The need for review was recognized by the establishment of a Patent Advisory Panel under the Federal Council for Science and Technology. The Patent Advisory Panel, under the Chairmanship of Dr. William Eaton, Deputy Assistant Secretary of Commerce for Science and Technology, is charged with the responsibility of:

—developing by mutual consultation with the agencies common guidelines for the implementation of the policy, consistent with existing statutes and providing over-all guidance as to disposition of inventions and patents in which the government has any right or interest; and

—encouraging the acquisition of data by government agencies on the disposition of patent rights to inventions resulting from federally financed research and development and on the use and practice of such inventions, to serve as a basis for policy review and development; and

—making recommendations for advancing the use and exploitation of government-owned domestic and foreign patents.

The Federal Council, in consultation with the Department of Justice, is required to report at least annually on the effectiveness of the policy, including recommendations for revision or modification.

Development of interpretive bulletins and guidelines through the mechanism of the Patent Advisory Panel is far from simple because of the differing missions and traditional philosophies of the various federal departments and agencies. Nonetheless, this appears to be the only way in which a fair degree of consistency and adherence to the policy can be achieved. Everything must be done to avoid narrow construction and restrictive interpretations which will not only delay and add to the cost of federal research and development programs, but will also inhibit the utilization of inventions through the incentives of the patent system and our free-market economy. Unless positive results are achieved by the Advisory Panel and Federal Council, they will lose the opportunity "for a trial in the light of facts and experience accumulated" before Congressional action is taken on government patent policy legislation.

In the Congress, the problem of patent policy by amendment continues. During this past year—in spite of the fact that the Kennedy Statement is fully supported by President Johnson—the so-called "title" proponents in the Senate attempted to add restrictive title provisions in virtually every Bill authorizing federal research and development. Because of the traditional position of the House, which generally favors the "license" approach, we were successful in eliminating the title provision from the Mass Transportation Act and the Clean Air Act.

On the Water Resources Research Act, S. 2, we succeeded in amending the provisions of the Senate Bill, to provide that the Act would be administered in accordance with the President's policy. Unfortunately, the Senate position prevailed in Conference. In this instance, the Bureau of the Budget stated the official position of the Administration that the restrictive patent provisions of S. 2 should be removed. The President's Science Advisor sent his personal congratulations following House action to amend the legislation. This is an added indication of Dr. Hornig's position on the government's patent policies and supports his previous testimony before my Subcommittee emphasizing the importance of further study of the issue. Action taken on this bill was a clear case of a strong title proponent facing a somewhat indifferent group of House conferees and, quite naturally, prevailing.

There is ample evidence that the small but dedicated group in the Senate who are overwhelmed by the "monopoly" aspects of the issue will continue to press for adoption of a government title clause in virtually every instance. We need to educate more Members of Congress to the full impact of such a policy and the realization that it will, in the words of the Budget Bureau, "inhibit the desired flexibility of the Administration's policy with respect to patent rights."

It is also clear that a new front has been opened by the publication of the Kennedy Patent Memorandum. Although the intent seems clear to me, we recently had an instance of a government agency promulgating restrictive patent regulations, not in keeping with the Policy, and without legal authority. Last year Congress passed a law authorizing aid to Commercial Fisheries Research; the bill contained no patent provisions. The Department of the Interior issued regulations to carry out the Act. In so doing, legal counsel in that Department used the general authority of the Act to assert the power to take title to new inventions, including those developed by State employees. I called this matter to the attention of the White House, and the Secretary of the Interior moved promptly to substitute language which invokes the Kennedy Patent Memorandum instead. I believe this is one of the first occasions on which the Presidential Memorandum has been specifically indicated as a guide to patent policy, and it is encouraging.

Congressional Outlook—89th Congress

Let us now turn to the outlook for patent policy legislation in the next Congress. As many of you know, the Senate Judiciary Subcommittee on Patents, Trademarks and Copyrights, held extensive hearings on several bills in 1961. Senator McClellan's subcommittee did not take any action on the proposed legislation because they were convinced that further study was needed and most important, "that a general title policy is not in the public interest." About this same time, our Subcommittee on Patents and Scientific Inventions was considering legislation to amend Section 305 of the Space Act. We had passed a similar bill in the House in 1960 but the Senate did not take action. Again, in 1962, we reported a bill to the Science and Astronautics Committee to amend these restrictive provisions but no further action was taken.

Early in 1963, several bills calling for a government-wide policy were introduced. Senator Russell Long again introduced his bill which calls for title-to-the-government of virtually all inventions and establishes a central government agency to manage and exploit the government's patent portfolio. Senator McClellan introduced S. 1290 which would establish a more flexible policy. Senator Leverett Saltonstall also introduced legislation somewhat similar to Senator McClellan's but including a provision for awards to inventors.

After the President's policy statement was issued, the Administration requested that no action be taken by the Congress until the policy had received a trial and experience was gained under its provisions. This, coupled with the fact that the Congress was tied up for so long with other important legislative matters, made hearings during the 88th Congress impractical.

There is every reason to believe, however, that this situation will not continue and that Congress will act, possibly as early as next year, on Government Patent Policy Legislation. Although there are many reasons for this prediction on my part, here are some of the major considerations:

—Opposition to the establishment of patent policy by the Executive Branch has already been expressed by Senators Long and Morse as well as others. The Space Administration was severely criticized for attempting to issue patent waiver regulations last year. And I recently saw a story to the effect that Senator Morse had objected rather violently to NASA's recent waiver proposals.

—The Annual Report of Senator McClellan's Subcommittee, in discussing the Administration's action on government patent policy, states that, "It is the view of the subcommittee that the former President's policy statement is a constructive contribution which will assist the subcommittee in acting upon the pending bills." The report goes on to say, however:

While differences exist as to what patent policy is desirable, the various actions of the Senate can leave no doubt but that the Senate is convinced that the broad outlines of patent policy *should be determined by the Congress.* This issue involves not only patents, but other questions of policy such as the expenditure of public funds, the progress of science, the encouragement of small business, the relationship between government and private industry, and the advancement of the economy by the transfer of research and development findings into commercially useful products and processes. *These policy matters properly come within the province of the legislative branch of government.*

—In addition, there are still on the books statutory provisions requiring patent practices in the space program, the atomic energy program, and a host of sundry programs in the natural resources and health fields which, in my opinion,

Damage small business, cost the taxpayer money, dilute the national effort to be first in scientific and technological accomplishments and waste the products of scientific research as a result of the reluctance to market new inventions without necessary patent protection.

These predictions do not mean that there is still not a long way to go before a reasonable and equitable government policy on the disposition of patent rights to inventions is achieved. Largely through the comprehensive hearings of our Subcommittee on Patents and Scientific Inventions, and hearings on government-wide patent policy by Senator McClellan's Subcommittee, there has evolved a much better understanding of the equities involved in government research and development contracting with private industry, universities and other research organizations.

From a position of not more than four years ago, when industry and government were poles apart on their views, substantial progress has been made through the normal, although admittedly slow, legislative process, aided by the Executive branch's development of patent policy regulations.

I will urge this audience to review patent policy legislation which will be introduced early in the next Congress, and give your elected representatives the benefit of your informed opinion. My own tentative conclusions from the detailed reviews which we have made, include these points:

(1) Few people really want a government title policy across the board.
(2) Nothing indicates that a government title policy would help the government reach its assigned research and development goals.
(3) Industry, through its developing incentive plans, has been making a

concerted effort to ameliorate criticism leveled at its handling of its own research employees.

(4) It is not the large industrial firms which will suffer the most if the government insists on all commercial rights to inventions produced under its research contracts. The subcontractor in most instances falls into the category of small business and is the one who is going to be caught in the middle. He is the one who depends most upon the commercial rights in his inventions to keep his organization going, and to protect himself from infringement after developing a good patent position or a saleable commercial product. The old established firms with secure background patent situations and strong financing do not have this worry to the same extent.

In conclusion, let me suggest that this battle is an honest one, in search of a fair and equitable policy. Those who fear the evil of monopoly, are simply exercising a legitimate concern of Government. Their concern is genuine, and their basic success is vital to the welfare of the country.

On the other hand, we must not lose sight of the provisions set down in the United States Constitution almost two hundred years ago, provisions which authorize the Congress to grant limited monopolies to creative persons in order to foster the arts and sciences. The precepts on which those principles were based are as valid and as important today as they were in 1787.

I am confident that the work which has been done in recent years, and to which many of you have contributed, is bearing fruit. We are seeing the crystallization of an equitable approach to patent policy. It is not yet firm, and we welcome thoughtful and useful contributions in the time ahead.

Continuing the discussion of patents, W. Halder Fisher adds a brief statement about the ownership of patent rights on federally-financed inventions. He studies the meaning of the word "patent" and its origin and development in English and American practice. He argues strongly that the only sensible general patent practice is for patents to be privately titled. He calls the practice of federal titling "dangerous and anomalous."

W. HALDER FISHER is Senior Research Economist with the Battelle Memorial Institute. He received a B.S. degree in Chemistry and Mathematics from the University of Richmond in 1934; and M.A. in Economics in 1943 and a Ph.D. in Economics and Sociology in 1945, both from the University of Virginia. His current assignment with Battelle is studying the effects of technology on the economy of the future. His immediate concern is with the projection of consumption patterns of various social economic groups for the year 1975.

CHAPTER 6

A NOTE ON THE
MEANING OF PATENTS

W. Halder Fisher

In recent months, several serious questions have arisen concerning the ownership of *patent rights* on federally financed inventions or on inventions involved in federal procurement contracts. If resolved in one way, these questions can greatly strengthen the United States patent system; but if resolved in another way, they can destroy it and more. We need a proper resolution of this problem. Therefore we should examine it carefully.

The Current Patent Controversy

Under the Atomic Energy Act of 1954 and the National Aeronautics and Space Act of 1958, the federal government has tended to pursue the policy of taking direct title to all patents developed by private parties in conjunction with government-financed research and procurement contracts. Moreover, in many instances, the policy has been extended to cover federal confiscation of all so-called "background" patents used in connection with government-financed contracts. On the other hand, the Department of Defense generally has followed the policy of allowing the private inventor to take title to all patents developed in connection with DOD-administered contracts, while protecting the government's interests by another device: retention of a royalty-free non-exclusive license covering all government uses.

In several recent sessions of Congress, bills have been introduced proposing a uniform federal policy with respect to these patent usages. Typical are the Long bill (S. 1176) and the McClellan bill (S. 1084) both of which embody the idea that, since the government has financed the research, the government should *own* all patents resulting from it.

There are many aspects of the patent system, of patent law, and of federal procurement which are highly relevant to any consideration of the issues raised by these bills. Most of these points have been expounded at great length by advocates on one side of this argument or the other. For some reason, however, neither side has gone systematically behind the immediate controversy to clarify certain of the basic concepts around which it rages. This relatively unexplored area provides the subject of my present inquiry.

What Was and Is a Patent?

⌐ The word *patent* has an interesting history in Anglo-Saxon law. Beginning long before the modern era, it was a well-established practice for the Sovereign to grant property or privilege to favored subjects, usually in return for or in anticipation of some exceptional service. The device by which such a grant was formalized came to be known as "Letters Patent" (that is, *open* letters) which began typically with a salutation equivalent to our modern phrase, "To whom it may concern,—."

The important thing about this practice was that the sovereign—answerable (by definition) only to God—granted a part of his sovereignty to the subject, be it the right to use a piece of land, the right to carry on a particular enterprise usually reserved to the Crown, the right to use a particular heraldic device or a particular title, or the right to spend a sum of money from the royal exchequer. The patent conveyed a *right*. That right *had* belonged exclusively to the *sovereign*. But the subject who received the right (that is, the bit of sovereignty) was in no way altered in his ultimate position as a subordinate subject.

This fact leads us to a conclusion which is highly relevant to the present situation: namely, that the sovereign would never have an occasion to confer a right upon *himself*—he already had it. What's more, as we shall see, he never wholly gave it away. This is to say that the whole purpose of a *patent* was, is and must be to convey to a subject (i.e., a private party) a restricted version of a right already possessed by the sovereign (the federal government).

In other words, when the sovereign takes title to a patent, the patent no longer exists—so why issue it in the first place?

The objection may be raised that this is not England, that we have no divinely-ordained sovereign, and that the private party is not a subject in the above sense. A moment's thought however, makes it clear that this argument leads only to the ultimate absurdity that the federal government does not possess the power to grant a patent!

What right is conveyed by a patent, in our present context? Simply the right to maintain a monopoly (limited in time and subject to other limitations imposed by the law) on the use of an *invention* or a new contribution to the arts. If the government does not want private parties to maintain such monopolies, it has only to refuse to issue the patents, thereby throwing those discoveries into the public domain.

The United States Patent System

In the formative days of the United States, the Founding Fathers faced up to many practical problems, solving them, often most creatively, by a combination of experience and ingenuity. The Constitutional Convention realized the need for fostering inventiveness for the economic wellbeing of the future nation and decided that Congress should have the power and the duty to promote the progress of science and the arts by securing to inventors and authors exclusive (for a period) rights to their own works (*Constitution,* Article 1, Section 8, Clause 8). In 1790 the Patent Office was established by statute based directly upon this constitutional mandate.

When it established the patent system, Congress drew directly or indirectly upon the English concept of the "letters patent." The purpose for which these patents were to be used was different from that of the original model; and the sovereign body issuing them was not a king (of divine origin). Nevertheless, the parallel between the English pattern and the American adaptation is completely clear.

Some Further Considerations

A paragraph, above, introduced the phrase "the public domain," a term which deserves closer examination. In common law, this phrase denotes all rights not reserved to specific private persons (or groups), but open to all *at the will of the sovereign.* In the United States, this means that the "public domain" is everybody's domain unless access is limited by law. A street or highway is in the public domain. Anyone can use it as long as he does so properly in the prescribed manner—which includes *not* using it when a police car or fire truck or military convoy or other public vehicle is on official emergency duty.

When the government finds, at a later point in time, that a private use-right which was granted earlier stands in the way of an important public use, a common-law corrective is always available. This is the power of "eminent domain," the procedure by which a private right (previously granted by the sovereign) can be, as it were, recalled to the public domain. Eminent domain (operating through *condemnation* proceedings) provides an orderly way of reasserting prior sovereignty. As a protection against arbitrary and unjustified assertions of public power, however, owners who have not abused their rights must be reimbursed for giving them up, the cost to the state being determined by a specially-convened condemnation court.

In U.S. patent law, the procedure by which a patent may be revoked is set forth in detail which has been elaborated by statute and adjudication. However, for reasons that will become clear, we have attempted to go *behind* this particular structure to the more fundamental concepts from which it derives.

We have now extended our understanding of the essential meaning of *patents* in several significant directions. At this point a recapitulation is in order:

1. A patent is a grant by the sovereign body to a private citizen of some part of its sovereign power.
2. It is an anomaly—in fact an absurdity—to say that the sovereign body should make a general practice of granting itself patents.
3. Moreover, when the state (the sovereign body) for any reason takes title to a patent, it thereby *destroys* the patent—in fact and without regard for legalisms—and throws that specific right back into the public domain.
4. Any right in the public domain is freely available to all, subject only to whatever specific limitations have been imposed by law upon that availability.
5. Any right (patent or other) which has been granted by the state can

be recalled by the state. The orderly recall of such a right is provided for generally by the assertion, through condemnation proceedings, of the power of eminent domain.

6. When a right is recalled by the state from a prior holder who has not abused it, due legal process requires that the owner be reimbursed, and the law of condemnation provides for the orderly determination of the amount of recompense.

Applications

Before specifically applying these generalizations to the current controversy, one further proviso should be stated: We cannot say that United States patent law is bound for all time by the implications of its common law background,—*but* we can say that it should never hastily or thoughtlessly break continuity with that background. Where newly-emerged needs can be met by devices which are compatible with the past, the use of those devices, in preference to others, will avoid confusion and will conserve our legal heritage.

In the current patents controversy, the point of conflict is whether the United States should *generally* follow the practice of taking title to all patents resulting from research conducted in conjunction with federal research and/or procurement contracts.

According to both our common-law heritage and the implicit nature of patents, the general answer must be that it should not.

The fundamental purpose of our patent system is to reserve to the inventor or discoverer, not to the government, an exclusive (but limited) right to the use of his invention or discovery. This purpose derives directly from the constitutional intention to promote progress through private endeavor.

Moreover, the essential nature of a patent makes it a grant by the sovereign body *to a citizen* (a subject) and not to itself. Nothing can be gained by the state giving itself something which it already has (a right); but much can be lost if the state makes a general practice of arbitrarily taking from its citizens something which it did not have (a valuable *idea*).

In the last analysis, when the state takes title to a patent, it throws the patented invention into the public domain. In other words, it condemns without judicial determination of the proper amount of compensation. And that is a violation of a very fundamental precept of our legal structure.

We have not yet looked at those special needs of the current situation which give rise to the present controversy; and conceivably they may force us to alter our general conclusion somewhat. Many of the areas in which federal titling of patents is now practiced are fraught with national defense and security considerations. They involve nuclear applications, new weapon development, space-craft, and the like. In many instances it is necessary that the agency exert absolute control over every access to and application of these inventions. Where this is the case, obviously an overriding new consideration enters the picture.

Nevertheless, wherever the national defense and security purpose can be achieved by special laws—for instance, drastic limitations imposed upon the title-holder—these devices should be used. Only in exceptional cases, cases for which no other solution is possible, should the government take the dangerous and anomalous step of federal titling.

Much of the present pressure toward federal titling, however, is based on more general considerations. "What the government helps finance, the government should own" is a dangerous general precedent to establish. For instance, it would imply that the Department of Agriculture should take title to all farm land upon which soil-conservation moneys have been expended and to all forest lands which have been federally reforested. Likewise, the Post Office Department should take title to all steamship lines, airlines, and railroads which have received federal subsidies for carrying the mail. Why should specific private individuals or firms be given exclusive right to profit from the expenditure of public funds? Obviously, if the premise for general federal titling of patents based on federal contracts is carried to its ultimate conclusion, the private sector of our society would shrink quite rapidly.

Conclusions

In brief, the common-law background of our patent system indicates that the only sensible general patent practice is for all patents to be privately titled, except where over-riding national defense and security needs justify confiscation. And then, proper compensation should be made.

The rationalizations which have been advanced for federal titling of all patents granted in conjunction with federally-financed research and/or procurement contracts are not only spurious, but are destructive of our whole system of private property. If this system, a fundamental of our society, is to be done away with, the action should be direct and open—not through this particular back door.

This chapter by Edwin Mansfield covers not only the sources of invention but further deals with eight other major issues involved in technical change and research and development. This impressive and comprehensive literature survey is a report of the author's research for the Carnegie Foundation. He also suggests paths for future research in this area. Because this paper touches on such a number of topics dealt with by the other contributors, it is a logical link between Parts I and II of this volume.

EDWIN MANSFIELD is Professor of Economics at the Wharton School of the University of Pennsylvania. He graduated with an A.B. from Dartmouth, and received his M.A. and Ph.D. in Economics from Duke. He also serves as consultant to the Rand Corporation, the Federal Power Commission and the Department of Commerce. He is editor of *Monopoly Power and Economic Performance*, and author of "Size of the Firm, Market Structure and Innovation" in the *Journal of Political Economy*, 1963.

CHAPTER 7

THE ECONOMICS OF RESEARCH AND DEVELOPMENT: A SURVEY OF ISSUES, FINDINGS, AND NEEDED FUTURE RESEARCH*

Edwin Mansfield

INTRODUCTION

This paper surveys the literature regarding the organization, administration, and economic effects of research and development; and outlines the types of further research that, in my opinion, are needed.[1] More specifically, the paper discusses the following nine topics: (1) the relationship between the size and organization of a society's R and D activities and its rate of economic growth; (2) the sources and timing of invention; (3) the relationship between the market structure of an industry and the size and effectiveness of its research activities; (4) the efficient management within the firm of industrial research and development; (5) the extent to which Fed-

---

* This paper draws freely on my unpublished report "Organization, Administration, and Economic Effects of Research and Development," which was commissioned by the Carnegie Corporation of New York.

[1] Needless to say, this survey must be both brief and selective. In the allotted space it would be impossible to cover all the relevant or important aspects of the economics of research and development. Moreover, the recommendations for future research are necessarily quite general, not detailed descriptions of specific projects.

107

eral support for civilian technology may be warranted; (6) the problems involved in the way defense and space R and D have been managed; (7) the impact of defense and space R and D on civilian technology; (8) the alleged shortage of scientists and engineers; and (9) the diffusion of the results of R and D.

R AND D AND ECONOMIC GROWTH

In recent years, there has been an enormous increase in the amount of attention devoted by social scientists, government officials, businessmen and others to the subject of economic growth. In government and elsewhere, there has been the feeling that the American economy is not growing as rapidly as it should. Partly in response to this, several studies have been made of the relative importance in the past of various factors which influence the rate of economic growth in the U.S. Despite differences in the techniques and data, these studies, by Abramowitz,[2] Denison,[3] Fabricant,[4] Massell,[5] and Solow,[6] reach generally similar results. Apparently, only about twenty percent of the increase in output per worker since 1900 can be explained by increases in equipment per worker. The rest is due to many factors, but the effects of technological change seem particularly important.[7]

This finding has led economists and others to consider more deeply the problems of measuring the rate of technological change and of determining the effects of various factors which influence this rate. In previous years, numerous attempts had been made, particu-

---

[2] M. Abramowitz, "Resource and Output Trends in the U.S. since 1870," *American Economic Review*, 1956.

[3] E. Denison, *The Source of Economic Growth in the United States*, Committee for Economic Development, 1962.

[4] S. Fabricant, *Basic Facts on Productivity Change* (Princeton: National Bureau of Economic Research, 1959).

[5] B. Massell, "Capital Formation and Technological Change in United States Manufacturing," *Review of Economics and Statistics*, 1960.

[6] R. Solow, "Technical Change and the Aggregate Production Function," *Review of Economics and Statistics*, 1957.

[7] See Griliches for a somewhat different approach. J. Griliches, "The Sources of Measured Productivity Growth: U.S. Agriculture, 1940–60," *Journal of Political Economy*, August, 1961.

larly by Kuznets,[8] Merton,[9] Schmookler,[10] and others, to use patent statistics and simple productivity indexes to measure the rate of technical change. Now more sophisticated techniques have been developed by Solow,[11] Kendrick,[12] and others. Using such measures, Minasian,[13] Mansfield,[14,15] and Terleckij[16] have conducted studies to determine the effect of an industry's (or firm's) level of R and D expenditures on its rate of technical change, the findings provide some quantitative estimates of the magnitude of this effect.

These studies, unfortunately, provide far less information than is needed to determine the total amount of money that society should devote to R and D to support a desired rate of economic growth. Moreover, they provide too little information to determine the optimal distribution of this total among various industries, and so on. To answer these questions, which are of course the crucial ones for public policy in this area,[17] one must have the answers to the following three sub-questions: First, how does the productivity of R and D vary among different sorts of research organizations—large, small, production-affiliated, independent, centralized, decentralized, government laboratory, and so on? What sort of organization and what scale of operations is most effective in carrying out R and D of

---

[8] S. Kuznets, "Inventive Activity; Problems of Definition and Measurement," *The Rate and Direction of Inventive Activity* (Princeton: Princeton University Press, 1962).

[9] R. Merton, "The Rate of Industrial Invention," *Quarterly Journal of Economics,* May, 1935.

[10] J. Schmookler, "Changes in Industry and the State of Knowledge as Determinants of Industrial Invention," *The Rate and Direction of Inventive Activity* (Princeton: Princeton University Press, 1962).

[11] R. Solow, *op. cit.*

[12] J. Kendrick, *Productivity Trends in the United States* (Princeton: National Bureau of Economic Research, 1961).

[13] J. Minasian, "The Economics of Research and Development," *The Rate and Direction of Inventive Activity* (Princeton: Princeton University Press, 1962).

[14] E. Mansfield and R. Brandenburg, *The Allocation and Characteristics of the Firm's R and D Budget: A Case Study* (Cambridge: Harvard University Press, 1964).

[15] E. Mansfield, "Industrial Research Expenditures: Determinants, Prospects and Relation to Size of Firm and Inventive Output," *Journal of Political Economy* (forthcoming).

[16] N. Terleckij, *Sources of Productive Growth,* Unpublished Ph.D. thesis.

[17] For a discussion of some of the relevant policy questions, see J. Dupre and E. Gustafson, "Contracting for Defense: Private Firms and the Public Interest," *Political Science Quarterly,* 1962.

various kinds? The answer to this question is needed if the nation's R and D, whatever its total amount, is to be allocated efficiently.

Second, given that R and D expenditures are allocated efficiently among various economic units,[18] what is the relationship between the total amount spent on R and D and the rate of technical progress? Obviously, since the amount spent on R and D influences the rate of economic growth via its effect on the rate of technical progress, it is necessary that we have the answer to this question, too. Third, to obtain the desired rate of economic growth, what combinations of the rate of investment, the rate of technical progress, and other key variables are required? The answer to this question is needed in order to find the "trade-offs," or rates of substitution, between the various factors that influence the rate of growth, a knowledge of such "trade-offs" being necessary if the desired rate of growth is to be achieved at minimum social cost.

These questions are extremely general. What are some more specific areas where research is needed? First, much more work should be done to develop better methods of measuring the rate of technical change in the economy, an industry, or a firm. As matters stand, almost all of our more sophisticated measures make the stringent assumptions that technical change is neutral, that it is cost-reducing, and that there are constant returns to scale. In order to answer the questions posed above, it obviously is necessary that we be able to relax such assumptions.

Second, attempts should be made to estimate the extent to which technical change in various industries in recent years has been neutral, labor-saving, or capital-saving. Although practically all of our more sophisticated models of technical change and economic growth assume that it is neutral, this may be quite far from the case. It would obviously be useful to have even rough estimates of the extent of the bias, the importance of which has been stressed by Fellner[19,20] and others. Some work along this line has been done by

---

[18] Such an allocation would be defined, of course, on the basis of the answer to the first question.

[19] W. Fellner, "Does the Market Direct the Relative Factor-Saving Effects of Technological Progress," *The Rate and Direction of Inventive Activity, op. cit.*

[20] W. Fellner, *Trends and Cycles in Economic Activity* (New York: Holt, Rinehart & Winston, 1956).

Brown and de Cani[21,22] and Resek[23] but much more study is needed.

Third, attempts should be made to estimate the extent to which technical change in selected industries in recent years has required new plant and equipment, the extent to which it could be "grafted" onto old plant and equipment and the cost of doing so, and the extent to which it could occur without altering existing plant and equipment. This question is important in formulating an answer to the third question above.[24] At present, there are two alternative models of economic growth, one presuming that technical change occurs without new investment[25] and one presuming that it occurs only as a consequence of new investment.[26] They provide quite different estimates of the effects of capital formation and expenditures on R and D on the rate of economic growth.

Fourth, detailed studies are needed to determine more precisely what is included as "R and D" in various industries. One of the important existing barriers to a better understanding of the relationship between R and D expenditures and the rate of technical change, is our ignorance of what R and D, as measured by the customary figures, is. We need a finer breakdown and characterization of the activities currently lumped together under the title of "R and D." What proportion is really routine service work? What proportion is aimed at particular types of new products and product improvements? What proportion is work aimed merely at monitoring various scientific fields? How long-term are the projects? How predictable are the results?

Fifth, we know very little about the effect of the composition of a firm's R and D projects on its rate of technical progress, as measured by a trend term in the production function. There have been a few

[21] M. Brown and J. de Cani, "Technological Change and the Distribution of Income," *International Economic Review*, September, 1963.

[22] M. Brown, "A Measure of Technological Employment," *Review of Economics and Statistics*, November, 1963.

[23] R. Resek, "Neutrality of Technical Progress," *Review of Economics and Statistics*, February, 1963.

[24] For a contrary view, see Edward Denison's comments in the March, 1964 *American Economic Review*.

[25] R. Solow, *op. cit.*

[26] R. Solow, "Investment and Technical Progress," *Mathematical Methods in the Social Sciences* (Stanford: Stanford University Press, 1959).

attempts to link a firm's total expenditures on R and D to its rate of technical change, but none of these studies has tried to disaggregate the total expenditures, which are notoriously heterogeneous, into more meaningful categories. Making various simple assumptions about the way in which various kinds of R and D expenditures enter the production function, it should be possible to make such an attempt. The results, despite their roughness, would be extremely useful, since they would help to indicate whether firms currently overinvest in one kind of research and underinvest in another. Finally, there are other areas where research might be carried out, but since they also fall under the topics considered in subsequent sections, they will be taken up there.

THE SOURCES AND TIMING OF INVENTION

Recent years have seen considerable work also regarding the sources and timing of invention. First, there have been studies of the importance of the corporation and the independent inventor as sources of important inventions. The important thing that must be stated in this connection is that, despite the many attempts to administer the last rites to the independent inventor, he is by no means dead. Over the last sixty years, it appears that the independent inventor has contributed a great deal to the stream of important inventions, particularly in industries not directly connected with the sciences. In their study of fifty significant twentieth-century inventions, Jewkes, Sawers, and Stillerman[27] estimate that over half were produced by individuals not doing company-directed research.

Nonetheless, this century has seen a notable shift in the source of inventions away from the independent inventor and toward the corporation. In 1900, about 80 percent of all patents were issued to individuals; in 1957, about 40 percent were issued to them.[28] The reasons for this shift are not difficult to find. Technology in most industries has become more complex, a division of labor among specialists in various scientific fields has become more necessary, and the instruments required to research and develop new processes and products have become more expensive.

[27] J. Jewkes, D. Sawers, and R. Stillerman, *The Sources of Invention* (New York; Macmillan Co., 1958).

[28] This excludes patents issued to government.

Second, there have been studies of the occupational, educational, and age characteristics of inventors. Schmookler[29] recently investigated the occupational characteristics of a random sample of about 100 persons granted patents in 1953. His results indicate that about 60 percent were engineers, chemists, metallurgists, and directors of research and development and that most of the rest were executives. Almost none were ordinary production workers. He also concludes that "as a rough approximation, only about forty percent of the inventors taking out patents in a given month are fulltime inventors (research and development technologists), about twenty or twenty-five percent are industrial personnel hired partly to invent, and about a third are completely independent inventors."

With regard to educational background, he found that about 16 percent (of those answering the question) had not completed high school, that 19 percent had completed high school but had not completed college, that 31 percent had finished college but had gone no further, and that 25 percent had gone on to do graduate work. Thus, although most had at least a college education, over one-third of these inventors had no more than a high school education.

Turning to the age of inventors, Lehman[30] has made a very interesting study of their age when they made "very important" and "important" inventions. Adjusted for the relative number alive at various ages, the mean age of inventors when they made "very important" inventions was 30–34 years. The mean age of the inventors of "important" inventions was about 37 years. These results are similar to the earlier findings of Spooner[31] and Rossman.[32] The most significant inventions seem to be largely the product of relatively young men.

Let us consider next the timing of inventions, as measured by patent statistics. Studies by Kuznets,[33] Mansfield,[34] Merton,[35]

[29] J. Schmookler, "Inventors Past and Present," *Review of Economics and Statistics,* August, 1957.

[30] H. Lehman, *Age and Achievement* (Princeton: Princeton University Press, 1953).

[31] T. Spooner, "Age of Invention," *Technology Review,* November, 1946.

[32] M. Rossman, *The Psychology of the Inventor* (Inventors Publishing Co., 1931).

[33] S. Kuznets, *Secular Movements in Production and Prices* (Boston: Houghton, Mifflin Co., 1930).

[34] E. Mansfield, "Innovation and Technical Change in the Railroad Industry," *Universities-NBER Conference on Transportation Economics,* 1963.

[35] R. Merton, "The Rate of Industrial Invention," *Quarterly Journal of Economics,* May, 1935.

Schmookler,[36,37] and Stafford[38] seem to indicate a tendency, ignoring short-term variation, for the rate of patenting in an industry to increase first at an increasing rate, then at a decreasing rate, and finally to decline. Specifically, the amount of patenting seems to be highly correlated with the output and investment of the industry, the number of patents granted per year increasing as the industry's output and investment increases and decreasing when the industry's output and investment declines. Moreover, according to Griliches and Schmookler,[39] the patent rate tends to lag behind the investment rate. Turning from long-run to short-run variations in the patent rate, there seems to be a tendency for the number of patents granted per year to rise and fall with the business cycle.[40]

One important use of research concerning the sources and timing of invention is to provide clues as to the relative efficiency of various institutional arrangements, industrial settings, educational backgrounds, and other factors, in promoting invention. Moreover, by pinpointing where the inventor is located in the society, it makes it easier for public policy to be formulated so as to encourage invention. Although previous work has been useful for these purposes, it seems clear that much more work, and work of a somewhat different kind, is called for, if the full potential of such studies is to be met.

First, more work should be carried out to investigate the motivation of the inventor, both independent and corporate employee. Some work of this sort has been carried out, but more penetrating analyses could be made if psychologists, as well as sociologists and economists, helped design and carry out the studies. More work on motivation is necessary if we are to understand the effects of public policies (like tax legislation) and management policies (like incentive systems) on inventive output.

[36] J. Schmookler, "Changes in Industry and the State of Knowledge as Determinants of Industrial Invention," op. cit.

[37] J. Schmookler, "Economic Sources of Inventive Activity," Journal of Economic History, March, 1962.

[38] A. Stafford, Trends of Invention in Material Culture, Ph.D. thesis, University of Chicago, 1950.

[39] J. Griliches and J. Schmookler, "Inventing and Maximizing," American Economic Review, September, 1963.

[40] E. Graue, "Inventions and Production," Review of Economics and Statistics, November, 1943.

Second, further attempts should be made to measure the psychological characteristics of inventors and to study the differences between productive, successful inventors and those that are less productive and successful. Studies along this line have been carried out by Mackinnon[41] and Rossman.[42] Moreover, there is the extensive body of literature on creativity, a survey of which has recently been provided by Golann.[43] Nonetheless, the existing works obviously only scratch the surface.

Third, further attempts should be made to describe in detail the history of technological change and invention in various industries. For example, the case studies by Jewkes, Sawers, and Stillerman,[44] Mueller,[45] Peck,[46] Enos,[47] Maclaurin,[48] and others, despite their many shortcomings, have been very useful and suggestive. Without a more sophisticated theory of invention and better techniques for measurement, such case studies must suffer from a certain arbitrariness and fuzziness. Nevertheless, they are likely to be useful in leading toward better theories and measurement procedures.

Fourth, and perhaps most important, attempts should be made to devise better theories of information, scientific discovery, and invention. Moreover, complementary attempts should be made to devise techniques to measure the crucial concepts and parameters in these theories. As matters now stand we have only the most rudimentary theories and techniques of measurement. Until "invention" is reduced somehow to measurable dimensions, limited progress can be made in this field.

---

[41] D. Mackinnon, "Intellect and Motive in Scientific Inventors: Implications for Supply," *The Rate and Direction of Inventive Activity* (Princeton: Princeton University Press, 1962).

[42] Rossman, *op. cit.*

[43] S. Golann, "Psychological Studies of Creativity," *Psychological Bulletin*, November, 1963.

[44] Jewkes, Sawers and Stillerman, *op. cit.*

[45] W. Mueller, "The Origins of the Basic Inventions Underlying DuPont's Major Product and Process Innovations, 1920–1950," *The Rate and Direction of Inventive Activity* (Princeton: Princeton University Press, 1962).

[46] M. Peck, "Inventions in the Postwar American Aluminum Industry," *The Rate and Direction of Inventive Activity, op. cit.*

[47] J. Enos, "Invention and Innovation in the Petroleum Refining Industry," *The Rate and Direction of Inventive Activity, op. cit.*

[48] W. Maclaurin, *Invention and Innovation in the Radio Industry* (New York: Macmillan Co., 1949).

TECHNICAL CHANGE AND BUSINESS CONCENTRATION

Another topic which has received considerable attention is the relationship between an industry's market structure—i.e., the extent to which it is dominated by a few large firms—and its rate of technical progress. This is a very important question since it indicates the extent to which a vigorous anti-trust policy promotes, or thwarts, rapid technical progress. There are well-respected economists on both sides of the question and little agreement to date.

In discussing this issue, it is advisable to distinguish between several related questions. First, what is the effect of an industry's market structure on the amount it spends on R and D? Although it is generally agreed that there is little incentive for a firm to carry out R and D in a perfectly competitive industry, there is considerable argument over whether or not an industry which is "relatively" competitive, but not perfectly so, will carry out more R and D than a "relatively" monopolistic industry.

On the one hand, Galbraith,[49] Schumpeter,[50] Villard,[51] and many others argue that an industry composed of large oligopolists will carry out more R and D than one composed of many smaller firms because a large oligopolist can finance R and D more easily and it can afford bigger projects. Moreover, ". . . its characteristically greater diversity means that the research results are more likely to be usable by it, its greater life expectancy permits it to wait longer for the payoff, and having a large share of the market, it can recapture a larger portion of the aggregate social gains from the research."[52]

On the other hand, others, like Jewkes,[53] Nutter,[54] and Schmookler[55] are not convinced that this is the case. They point out

---

[49] J. Galbraith, *American Capitalism* (Boston: Houghton, Mifflin Co., 1952).

[50] J. Schumpeter, *Capitalism, Socialism and Democracy* (New York: Harper & Row, Publishers, Inc., 1947).

[51] H. Villard, "Competition, Oligopoly, and Research," *Journal of Political Economy,* December, 1958.

[52] R. Nelson, "The Simple Economics of Basic Scientific Research," *Journal of Political Economy,* June, 1959.

[53] Jewkes, Sawers and Stillerman, *op. cit.*

[54] O. Nutter, "Monopoly, Bigness, and Progress," *Journal of Political Economy,* June, 1959.

[55] J. Schmookler, "Bigness, Fewness, and Research," *Journal of Political Economy,* December, 1959.

that, in oligopolistic and monopolistic industries, there may be less pressure to do research; and they present data showing that, above some minimum size, there is little or no relationship in various industries between the amount spent on R and D as a percent of sales and a firm's size. Going a step further, Mansfield[56] has shown that in most of the industries for which he had data, the largest firms spent a smaller proportion of their sales on R and D than did their somewhat smaller rivals.

Second, what is the effect of an industry's market structure on the productivity of a given amount spent on R and D? There are numerous reasons for believing that there are economies of scale in research and development up to some point. The advantages of large size stem from the "lumpiness" of capital equipment like cyclotrons, the advantages of specialization of scientific labor, and the fact that risks can be reduced by taking advantage of the law of large numbers. Given that these economies of scale exist, it may not be efficient to have a large number of research establishments in a given field.

Mansfield[57] provides some very tentative evidence regarding the extent of such economies of scale in the chemical, petroleum refining, and steel industries. He also notes that the productivity of a firm's R and D generally seems to decline as size of firm increases, the size of its R and D expenditures being held constant. Needless to say, these bits of evidence are not sufficient to answer the basic question. In a particular industry, although most observers would probably agree that there are economies of scale in R and D up to some point, there would probably be considerable disagreement about their extent and about the size of R and D establishment beyond which further increases in size brought little or nothing in the way of added efficiency.

Third, what is the effect of an industry's market structure on how rapidly new techniques and products, both those developed by the industry and those developed by others, are introduced commercially. Again, there is considerable disagreement. On the one hand,

---

[56] E. Mansfield, "Industrial Research Expenditures; Determinants, Prospects and Relation to Size of Firm and Inventive Output," *Journal of Political Economy* (forthcoming).

[57] *Ibid.*

there are some—like Bain,[58] Brozen,[59] Joan Robinson,[60] and Stocking[61]—who believe that inventions would be applied most rapidly under purely competitive conditions. They argue that if many firms exist, there is more protection against an invention's being blocked by the faulty judgment of only a few men. Moreover, they allege that the existence of many competitors will force a firm to seek out and apply new ideas, whereas a live-and-let-live policy may develop otherwise. On the other hand, there are others—like Villard[62]—who think that they would be applied most rapidly if industries contained relatively few large firms. They point out that such firms are better able to finance the introduction of inventions and to take the necessary risks, and they sometimes claim that the larger firms will have better managers who will be more inclined to innovate.

Here, as elsewhere, one thing that is badly needed is more empirical work. One of the few empirical studies carried out to date[63] indicates that the largest firms do a disproportionately large share of the innovating under some conditions, but not under others. Whether one type of market structure is better than another seems to depend on the size of the investment required to innovate and other such factors.

Fourth, what are the effects of an industry's market structure on how rapidly, once innovations are introduced, they spread throughout the industry? In this case, there seems to be somewhat greater agreement, most economists seeming to believe that greater concentration in an industry results in a slower rate of diffusion. However, the evidence for this proposition, discussed in Section 10 below, is quite limited.

What sorts of research need to be carried out in this area? First, attempts should be made to develop measures of inventive effort

---

[58] J. Bain, *Pricing, Distribution, and Employment* (New York: Holt, Rinehart & Winston, 1953).

[59] Y. Brozen, "Invention, Innovation and Imitation," *American Economic Review,* 1951.

[60] J. Robinson, *The Rate of Interest* (New York: Macmillan Co., 1952).

[61] O. Stocking, Testimony before Subcommittee on Study of Monopoly Power, Judiciary Committee, House of Representatives, 1950.

[62] Villard, *op. cit.*

[63] E. Mansfield, "Size of Firm, Market Structure, and Innovation," *Journal of Political Economy,* December, 1963.

which include the work of independent inventors and which are comparable for both large and small firms. The NSF data on research and development expenditures may be misleading when used to help answer the first question because some activities are called R and D by a large firm but something else by a small one. Of course, this is not an easy task, as Kuznets[64] and others have pointed out, but it nonetheless is an important one.

Second, further attempts should be made to measure the extent to which there are economies of scale in various kinds of R and D activities. Of course, studies of this sort immediately encounter the problems, discussed previously, of measuring inventive input and output. But results based on very rough measures would be useful. Available studies[65] indicate that the problems are by no means hopeless.

Third, further attempts should be made to identify the firms that pioneered in the introduction of the important new processes and products introduced in various industries. Some work along this line has been carried out by Mansfield,[66] Enos,[67] and others; but there is need for much more empirical work of this sort. Moreover, attempts should be made to generalize, extend, and refine existing models[68] devised to relate such data to problems of public policy.

Fourth, studies should be made of the effects of a firm's size on the composition of its R and D expenditures. Several attempts have been made to determine the relationship between a firm's size and the total amount it spends on R and D, but no attempt has been made to determine the equally important relationship between a firm's size and the nature of its R and D projects. Do the larger firms concentrate on different sorts of projects than the small firms? Do they accept more risky projects? More basic projects? Longer-term projects? It should be possible to obtain answers to these very important, and currently unanswered, questions.

Fifth, further attempts should be made to construct theoretical models of the diffusion process and to see how, according to these models, an industry's market structure influences the rate of diffu-

---

[64] Kuznets, "Inventive Activity; Problems of Definition and Measurement," *op. cit.*
[65] Mansfield, "Industrial Research Expenditures," *op. cit.*
[66] Mansfield, "Size of Firm, Market Structure, and Innovation," *op. cit.*
[67] Enos, *op. cit.*
[68] Mansfield, "Industrial Research Expenditures," *op. cit.*

sion. Moreover, more data should be gathered regarding the diffusion process. More will be said in this regard in Section 10 below.

THE MANAGEMENT OF INDUSTRIAL R AND D

There is an enormous literature on the organization and management of research and development carried on by industry.[69] General business journals like the *Harvard Business Review*, specialized journals like the *IRE Transactions on Engineering Management*, and a number of books and pamphlets have described and analyzed the situation and the problems involved. [e.g.[70,71,72,73,74]].

We have a reasonably adequate picture of the way in which the R and D activities of various firms are organized. The organization varies considerably from industry to industry, and from firm to firm, due in part to basic differences in the purposes for which the laboratories were created and the size of the firm. Some laboratories are engaged primarily in quality control and testing; others do more in the way of applied research and development leading to new processes and products or improvements in old ones; a few engage in basic research as well. Because of the lack of any satisfactory theory of the creative process, the lack of any really dependable rules of thumb with regard to research administration, and the inevitable uncertainties involved in R and D, the administration and control of a research laboratory tends to be looser and more informal than in most other areas of business. Although there may exist a rather formidable formal control structure, most of the operating decisions seem in fact to be made quite informally.

Ideas and proposals for R and D projects arise from many sources.

---

[69] A. Rubenstein, "Looking Around, Guides to R and D," *Harvard Business Review,* 1957.

[70] R. Anthony, *Management Controls in Industrial Research Organizations* (Cambridge: Harvard University Press, 1952).

[71] C. Furnas, *Research In Industry* (Princeton: D. Van Nostrand Co., Inc., 1948).

[72] D. Hertz, *Costs, Budgeting, and Economics of Industrial Research* (New York: Columbia University Press, 1951).

[73] D. Hertz, *The Theory and Practice of Industrial Research* (New York: McGraw-Hill Book Co., 1950).

[74] C. Mees and J. Leermakers, *The Organization of Industrial Scientific Research* (New York: McGraw-Hill Book Co., 1950).

Customers often point out, and press for, improvements in the firm's product. The sales and production divisions of the firm sometimes make suggestions. New developments in science or innovations made by competitors often stimulate new projects. Carter and Williams[75] summarize some figures indicating that, for the companies included in the relevant studies, about 50 percent of the research topics originated within the research departments, about 25 percent came from the sales department, and about 15 percent came from the production department. Of course, these figures are rough and they pertain only to a few firms.

To choose among alternative research proposals, many laboratories have some formal system whereby comparisons are made of the probability of success, the estimated cost of the project, and the estimated returns from the project if it is successful. Examples of these schemes are given in a 1954 National Science Foundation report;[76] and a detailed case study is contained in Mansfield and Brandenburg.[77] Other firms use no formal procedures of this sort, although they too seem generally to be motivated by profit considerations in choosing among projects. Of course, it is much easier to estimate the probable returns from a development project than a research project, so formal procedures for estimating expected rates of return are generally limited to development projects.

Interview studies and questionnaires designed to find out what factors determine the size of a firm's total expenditures on R and D suggest that firms base their decisions on the attractiveness of the suggested R and D projects, their sales, general business conditions, the research policies of other firms, and still other factors. Unfortunately, since these studies do not specify in detail how these factors influence a firm's R and D expenditures and since they provide no clue to the quantitative importance of each factor in various industries, they are not very useful as predictive models or as guides to public policy. To help fill this void, an econometric model[78] was

---

[75] C. Carter and B. Williams, *Industry and Technical Progress* (New York: Oxford University Press, 1957).

[76] National Science Foundation, *Science and Engineering in American Industry*, Washington, 1956.

[77] Mansfield and Brandenburg, *op. cit.*

[78] Mansfield, "Industrial Research Expenditures," *op. cit.*

constructed and tested to explain the level of a firm's privately-financed R and D expenditures. This model could fit quite well the historical data regarding the behavior of 35 firms in five industries.

The studies considered thus far in this section are concerned with the description of existing behavior and the measurement of the effects of various factors on how much is spent on R and D of various kinds. What do we know about the way in which R and D should be carried out? Unfortunately, the answer is very little. Although there has been a flood of articles which dispense wisdom regarding the administration of research, their scientific content is almost without exception very low. They provide neither the necessary theory from which one could derive optimal behavior nor any convincing empirical results indicating that certain decision rules are in fact better than others.

One of the few exceptions is the work carried out by Klein[79,80, 81,82,83,84,85] and his associates at the RAND Corporation. Given that the uncertainties involved in R and D are very great initially but that they diminish substantially as a project proceeds, they have shown that the optimal strategy in managing an R and D effort may be to run in parallel several projects designed to serve the same end. Further, under simplified conditions, they have determined the circumstances under which this is the optimal strategy and, given various relevant factors, the optimal number of parallel projects. Although this strategy may seem to involve needless and wasteful duplication of effort, under many circumstances it is in fact the cheapest way to proceed.

In this area, the following additional research seems very promising. First, it is important that better techniques be developed to

[79] B. Klein, "A Radical Proposal for R and D," *Fortune*, May, 1958.

[80] B. Klein, "The Decision Making Problem in Development," *The Rate and Direction of Inventive Activity, op. cit.*

[81] B. Klein and W. Mackling, "Applications of Operations Research to Development Decisions," *Operations Research*, May, 1958.

[82] T. Marschak, "Strategy and Organization in a System Development Project," *The Rate and Direction of Inventive Activity, op. cit.*

[83] A. Marshall and W. Meckling, "Predictability of the Costs, Time and Success of Development," *The Rate and Direction of Inventive Activity, op. cit.*

[84] R. Nelson, "The Link Between Science and Invention: The Case of the Transistor," *The Rate and Direction of Inventive Activity, op. cit.*

[85] R. Nelson, "Uncertainty, Learning and Economics of Parallel Research and Development Efforts," *Review of Economics and Statistics*, November, 1961.

measure the "output" of a firm's R and D effort. Without such measures, it is extremely difficult to tell whether one type of organization or management is better than another, because there is no reliable measuring rod.

Second, since work cannot stop while better techniques of measurement are being developed, attempts should be made to obtain the best possible measures, using existing techniques, of the "output" of a firm's R and D activities. Then these data should be analyzed to determine the effects of differences in organization and policy on the productivity of a firm's R and D effort. One possible course to take in this work would be to try to bring together and extend the measures of the profitability of their R and D establishment which have been made by various companies. Although they often are very crude, they would be a useful point of departure.

Third, it would be relatively simple to compare the firm's estimates made prior to the decision to carry out a project of the potential commercial value of a project and its technical feasibility with the outcome in these regards of the project. Such a study would throw considerable light on the extent to which a firm can forecast the potential benefits and costs of a proposed project, and the results would have obvious implications for project selection. The paper by Mansfield and Brandenburg[86] is a beginning, but it pertains to only one firm.

Fourth, it would also be useful to study the way in which projects are actually selected in a number of firms. Data could be obtained regarding the characteristics of projects that were accepted and those that were turned down, and a discriminant analysis (a particular kind of statistical technique) could be applied. Somewhat different, but related, techniques could be used to study the extent to which a project's budget was altered. Again, some work along this line has been done,[87] but it is only a beginning.

Fifth, much more work is needed to follow up Klein's ideas on parallel R and D efforts. As matters stand, there is no rigorous proof (or none that has been published) for his propositions, except in the simplest case. Much more theoretical work is needed.

Sixth, efforts should be made to put a broader theoretical basis under the empirically-determined learning curves discussed by

[86] Mansfield and Brandenburg, *op. cit.*

[87] Mansfield and Brandenburg, *op. cit.*

Asher[88] and others. They have not been integrated very well into the main stream of economics.

FEDERAL SUPPORT FOR CIVILIAN TECHNOLOGY

Can we rely on free enterprise to allocate resources efficiently in the area of inventive activity? Will enough research and development of the right sorts be carried out? There are at least two important reasons for believing that a free enterprise economy will generate less R and D than is socially desirable and that the deficiency will be particularly acute in the case of basic and more risky types of research.

First, it seems clear that there are considerable discrepancies between the private benefits that can be obtained from research results and the social benefits. This is because the results of R and D often are of little direct value to the firm sponsoring the R and D, but of great value to other firms, and because the benefits to other firms cannot easily be captured by the firm carrying out the R and D. This problem of "external economies" is particularly acute in the case of basic research.[89,90]

Second, it is often argued that because many firms are risk-averters and risks cannot be shifted completely and perfectly, there is a tendency for investment in risky activities to fall short of the social optimum, which is the point where expected returns equal the market rate of return, regardless of the variance. Arrow[91,92] and Nelson[93] present arguments to this effect.

Since both of these factors will result in too little being spent on R and D, it appears that, for an optimal allocation of resources, the government or some other agency not motivated by profit should finance additional research and development. In fact, of course, this has long been the case; and the more relevant question at this point is

---

[88] H. Asher, *Cost Quantity Relationships in the Airplane Industry*, (RAND Corporation, 1956).

[89] Nelson, "The Simple Economics of Basic Scientific Research," *op. cit.*

[90] C. Hitch, "Character of Research and Development in a Competitive Economy," *Proceedings of Conference on Research and Development*, National Science Foundation, 1958.

[91] K. Arrow, "Economic Welfare and the Allocation of Resources," *The Rate and Direction of Inventive Activity*, *op. cit.*

[92] Arrow, "Comment," *ibid.*

[93] Nelson, "The Simple Economics of Basic Scientific Research," *op. cit.*

not whether the government should support R and D but how much support it should give. Formally, it should push its contribution to the point where the expected marginal social benefit equals the social benefit in alternative uses, but obviously this is a very difficult thing to measure. Probably the most interesting attempt to measure the social rate of return from R and D is Griliches' study,[94] which concludes that the social rate of return from the investment in agricultural research has been very high.[95]

On the assumption that the social rate of return from additional R and D regarding civilian technology exceeds the social cost, the Department of Commerce submitted a civilian industrial technology program to Congress in 1963. This program had two broad purposes: "(a) to assist the continued and expanded use of technology for the upgrading of industrial practices, and (b) to encourage the development of an adequate supply of scientific and engineering personnel for the conduct of industrial research."[96]

To accomplish the purposes of this program, it was proposed that support be given to important industries, from the point of view of employment, foreign trade, etc., which have "limited or dispersed technological resources." Examples cited by the Administration included textiles, building and construction, machine tools and metal fabrication, lumber, foundries and castings. Federal support was to be given to the training of personnel at universities for industrial research and development, the proposed training being provided through research contracts at universities. Federal funds were to be used, wherever possible, to supplement new spending for these purposes by state and local governments.

In addition, federal support was to be given "to generate the technical work not called forth in sufficient quantity by the profit incentive alone, but necessary for the technological advancement of an industry or an industry segment, and to provide additional research services and facilities for those firms which do not have a broad enough spectrum of programs or services to support an

[94] J. Griliches, "Research Costs and Social Returns: Hybrid Corn and Related Innovations," *Journal of Political Economy*, October, 1958.

[95] For another, more recent study, see J. Griliches, "Research Expenditures, Education, and the Aggregate Agricultural Production Function," *Netherland School of Economics*, Report 6333.

[96] U.S. Department of Commerce, *The Civilian Industrial Technology Program*, Washington, D.C., 1963.

independent research and development program of efficient size."[97]

Further, it was proposed that an industry-university extension service be established, with the purpose of increasing the rate and extent of diffusion of technology throughout industry and of reducing the technical gap between the leading and lagging industries and firms. Modeled largely on the agricultural extension service, it called for: (1) field engineers attached to designated engineering schools; (2) visits to local industry to spread the latest technical information and to uncover problems requiring further research; (3) conferences, seminars, and demonstrations to disclose pertinent scientific and technical data to groups of firms with similar capabilities and interests; and (4) performance of technological research relating to major problems faced by the firm in the state.

This program stemmed in part from conclusions reached by the White House Panel on Civilian Technology, which was disbanded in 1962. Also, the National Academy of Sciences issued reports in 1962 that found that such support was needed in textiles and building.[98,99] In 1963, J. Herbert Hollomon, who headed the program asked Congress for $7.4 million to begin carrying out these proposals, but met with little success on Capitol Hill.

There are a number of important places in this area where further research is badly needed. First, despite a great deal of lip service being paid to "external economies" in R and D, we know very little about their extent in particular areas of the economy. In which industries and in what sorts of R and D are there large discrepancies between private and social benefits from R and D? How large are the differences between social and private rates of return?

Second, and related to the previous question, how can we measure the social returns from R and D of various kinds? Although this is a terribly difficult question, we cannot avoid it if we are to formulate sensible public policy. It is important that we be able to compare the benefits to be derived from an extra million dollars spent on research regarding transportation, textiles, communications, and other areas. It is also important that we compare the benefits to be derived from

[97] *Ibid.*

[98] National Academy of Sciences-National Research Council, *A Program for Building Research in the United States,* Washington, D.C., 1962.

[99] National Academy of Sciences-National Research Council, *Current Needs in Research Relevant to the Interests of the U.S. Textile Industry,* Washington, D.C., 1962.

such R and D with those to be derived from R and D concerning public health, education, and other areas in the public sector of the economy. To make a sensible allocation of the nation's R and D among alternative uses, it is necessary that we find some way to answer this question, at least roughly.[100]

Third, much more work is required to determine the sort of government action which will be the most effective and least costly way of stimulating the proper amount of extra R and D in those areas where too little is currently being spent. Should a tax credit be used? Or should matching grants be made to industry research associations? There have been some recent discussions of this within the Administration, but there has been little real study of the issues involved. It should be possible to obtain much more of the information that is needed.

Fourth, if matching grants are made to industry research organizations, how should these organizations be set up? Should there be government members on the boards of directors? How many? What principles should guide the selection of industries and projects? What devices should be set up to insure that the research results are used promptly and efficiently? These questions must be answered, if the Commerce program were to be adopted.[101]

Fifth, what sort of machinery can be established within a civilian technology program to evaluate its effectiveness in fairly unambiguous terms? In certain parts of this program it may be possible to evaluate the potential benefits after some small-scale experimentation has been carried out. In these areas, it is important that the right sorts of information be collected and used to guide future decisions regarding the proper size and orientation of the program.

THE MANAGEMENT OF MILITARY R AND D

In 1962, the Defense Department spent about $6.6 billion on research and development, over half of the total amount spent by the Federal government. The largest expenditures were made by the Air Force; the smallest were made by the Navy. Relatively little was

---

[100] For a recent attempt to develop methods of evaluating government R and D, see F. Scherer, *Measuring the Benefits of Government Research and Development Programs* (Washington, D.C.: Brookings Institution, 1963).

[101] Perhaps a study of the performance and problems of the organization set up in Great Britain would be useful. For some information regarding British experience see K. Gressfield, "Inventions as Business," *Economic Journal*, March, 1963.

spent on basic research, almost 90 percent of the total being devoted
to development. Because of security requirements, we know little
about many aspects of the R and D expenditures of the DOD.
Nonetheless, Congressional hearings and General Accounting Office
reports provide considerable information of a general nature; and
studies by the RAND Corporation,[102] the Harvard Weapons Acquisition Project,[103] and others have given us more detailed analyses. In
this section, I take up several characteristics of military R and D, as it
is currently organized, which are generally regarded as problem
areas.

First, there is the so-called "systems approach" to the procurement
of new weapons, which has been central to the way the services have
conducted this sort of procurement for the last decade. This approach is characterized by the great emphasis on planning from the
beginning of the various steps that must be carried out and the
sequencing of these steps which will minimize delay. According to a
representative of the DOD, "What distinguishes weapon systems
procurement is the same factor we have referred to repeatedly—
time. The same two basic factors, coordination and time phasing,
are overriding considerations in the procurement area just as
in the management area. Thus, we can plan, negotiate, and incorporate contractual provisions to assure compatibility of effort among
all participants in the program. Duplication of effort must also
be avoided. We cannot have a contractor, for example, designing a
subsystem comparable to one already developed. Contracts must be
placed for end items, subsystems, and support systems so as to insure
their availability at the proper time for integration into the weapon
system."[104]

The "systems approach" has come under considerable attack, the
principal critics being Klein,[105,106,107] Hitch,[108] and others associated

---

[102] Klein, "The Decision Making Problem in Development," *op. cit.*

[103] M. Peck and F. Scherer, *The Weapons Acquisition Process* (Boston: Harvard
Business School, 1961).

[104] *Procurement Study,* Hearings before the Procurement Subcommittee of the Committee on Armed Services, 86th Congress, Second Session, February 8–9, 1960, Part 1,
pp. 103–4.

[105] Klein, "Radical Proposal for R and D," *op. cit.*

[106] Klein, "The Decision Making Problem in Development," *op. cit.*

[107] Klein and Mackling, *op. cit.*

[108] Hitch, *op. cit.*

with the RAND Corporation. Using the results regarding parallel R and D efforts described in Section 5 above, they argue that the "systems approach" is inefficient. Although the scheduled completion dates may be met, at least approximately, costs tend to be very high and performance characteristics tend to be sacrificed. To buttress their case, RAND has made a number of case studies of the development of fighter planes, missiles, and other military hardware.

Second, there is the form of the contract used in military R and D. Typically, these contracts have been cost plus fixed fee, the limit on fees being 15 percent of estimated cost. Of course, the reasons for this kind of contractual arrangement, rather than a fixed price, were that the "product" that was being bought by the government could not be specified in advance with any accuracy and that the "product" of the work was so unpredictable that the risks to the seller would require a very high fixed price, if it were feasible at all.

The implications of CPFF contracts, as well as other varieties used in military contracting, have been analyzed by Moore,[109] Kaysen,[110] Dupre and Gustafson,[111] Scherer,[112] and others. Obviously, CPFF contracts, together with other aspects of the system, provide a strong incentive for contractors to understate costs at the design competition stage and no incentive to control them during development. The objections to such a system have often been raised in Congress and elsewhere. Recently, the DOD began to use incentive contracts, rather than CPFF contracts. There are enormous difficulties in the application of incentive contracting to R and D, and there is little information so far as to how it is working out.

Third, there is the treatment of patent rights to inventions made under procurement contracts. The present policy of the DOD, in contrast with the AEC, NASA, and other federal agencies, is to leave title to the patents in the hands of the contractors and reserve a royaltyfree and nonexclusive license providing for the use of any such invention for government purposes. This policy has been the

[109] Moore, *op. cit.*

[110] Kaysen, *op. cit.*

[111] J. Dupre and E. Gustafson, "Contracting for Defense: Private Firms and the Public Interest," *Political Science Quarterly*, 1962.

[112] F. Scherer, *The Weapons Acquisition Process: Economic Incentives* (Boston: Harvard Business School, 1964).

subject of much debate,[113] Senator Long being a particularly vehement critic of the DOD's policy. The evidence presented by Watson, Bright, and Burns[114] suggests that the importance of this issue may not be very great, although it is not entirely negligible.

Fourth, there is the organization of military R and D. Some have argued that, to a greater extent, research and development should be divorced from production responsibilities; and that the organizations doing R and D should receive long-term financial support. They believe that the nonprofit research institute or government laboratory would be superior means of conducting R and D, although business firms would obviously continue to do the production work.

Fifth, there are a number of important problems connected with the relationships that have grown up between the federal government, on the one hand, and industry and the universities on the other. With regard to government-industry relations, there are problems due to the fact that R and D contracts are concentrated very heavily in the largest firms and that industry sometimes exerts tremendous power to influence the choice of weapons systems. With regard to government-university relations, there are problems arising from the redirection of professional talent toward research and away from teaching, the concentration of grants and contracts in large universities, and such financial matters as the proper reimbursement for the universities' indirect costs. See[115,116,117,118,119].

Bearing in mind the sensitive nature of this area and the difficulty

[113] For example, see W. Leontief, "On Assignment of Patent Rights on Inventions Made Under Government Research Contracts," *Harvard Law Review,* January, 1964; L. Preston, "Patent Rights Under Federal R and D Contracts," *Harvard Business Review,* October, 1963; and the testimony in *"Economic Aspects of Government Patent Policies,"* Hearings before a Subcommittee of the Select Committee on Small Business, U.S. Senate, 1963.

[114] D. Watson, A. Bright and A. Burns, "Federal Patent Policies in Contracts for Research and Development," *The Patent, Trademark and Copyright Journal,* 1960.

[115] J. Dupre and S. Lakoff, *Science and the Nation* (Englewood Cliffs, N.J.: Prentice-Hall, Inc., 1962).

[116] F. Machlup, "Can There Be Too Much Research?" *Science,* 1958.

[117] F. Machlup, *The Production and Distribution of Knowledge in the United States* (Princeton: Princeton University Press, 1962).

[118] C. Kidd, *American Universities and Federal Research* (Cambridge: Harvard University Press, 1959).

[119] D. Price, J. Dupre, and W. Gustafson, "Current Trends in Science Policy in the United States," (*Impact of Science on Society,*1960).

of obtaining data, it should nonetheless be possible to carry out additional research regarding some of these questions. First, studies could be made of the decision-making process within the DOD, the kinds of considerations that affect R and D decisions, the kinds of pressures that are exerted, the sort of incentives of the various agencies within the government, the ways in which conflicts are resolved, etc. Some work along this line has been done by Cherington, Peck, and Scherer[120] and Enthoven and Rowen,[121] but much more should be done.

Second, further studies should be made of the effects of various kinds of contracts on R and D performance and costs. Scherer[122] has completed a very useful book on this subject. In addition, some theoretical and empirical work along this line has been done by the author and others in unpublished RAND memoranda. This work is only a beginning, but it does indicate how statistical decision theory, together with data regarding the outcome of past contracts, can be applied to throw new light on this problem.

Third, as suggested in previous sections of this paper, attempts should be made to extend the existing theory of parallel R and D efforts and to see the extent to which it is applicable to more realistic cases. Attempts should also be made to measure the productivity of the R and D carried out by various types of organizations. Admittedly, this is a formidable task, but without such measures, it is impossible to make an informed evaluation of recommendations like the fourth point above.

THE IMPACT OF MILITARY AND SPACE R AND D ON CIVILIAN TECHNOLOGY

During the past year or so, there has been a considerable amount of interest in the extent of the benefits to civilian technology—the "spillover" or "fallout"—from military and space R and D. NASA has been particularly interested in the extent of the "spillover," because if large, it would be an additional argument, besides the

---

[120] P. Cherington, M. Peck, and F. Scherer, "Organization and Research and Development Decision Making Within a Government Department," *The Rate and Direction of Inventive Activity, op. cit.*

[121] A. Enthoven and H. Rowen, "Defense Planning and Organization," *Public Finances: Needs, Sources and Utilization* (Princeton: Princeton University Press, 1962).

[122] Scherer, *op. cit.*

political and perhaps military ones, for its program. Numerous groups within the Administration, e.g., the White House Panel on Civilian Technology, have been interested in the extent of this "spillover," because of its implications regarding the extent to which civilian technology was really being drained of scientists and engineers by the military and space programs.

What is the value of the "spillover" from military and space R and D into the civilian economy? One definition of its value is the difference between the value of the goods and services produced in the civilian economy and the value of such production if no results from military and space R and D could have been used there. But this difference cannot be measured with any accuracy. The task seems impossible because of the many indirect benefits, because one would have to estimate when the same results would have been obtained without military or space R and D; and because the civilian research effort might well have proceeded in entirely different directions.

Is it possible to make a very rough appraisal of the past importance of the "spillover"? Perhaps a very rough lower bound can be obtained by taking various important inventions in the civilian economy that resulted from military and space R and D, estimating roughly how long it would have taken without such R and D to have obtained these inventions, and estimating the value of the extra product due to their having been available that much sooner. An important difficulty in this procedure is that it assumes that the course of technical change would have been the same in the civilian economy, if the results of military and space R and D had not been available, as it would have been otherwise.

Nonetheless, if this very crude method were applied, it seems likely that the estimated past value of the "spillover" would prove to be substantial. The electronic computer, ultrasonic testing, printed circuits, atomic energy, synthetic rubber, these and many other significant inventions stemmed from military R and D. Moreover, there is undoubtedly considerable opportunity for such "spillover" from current military and space R and D. For example, the space program may have important effects on civilian communication, weather prediction, medicine, power sources, metallurgy, and perhaps transportation.

Nonetheless, there seems to be a widespread feeling that the "spillover" per dollar of R and D is unlikely to be as great as in the past, because the capabilities that are being developed and the environment that is being probed are less intimately connected with civilian activities than formerly. The devices needed to send a man to the moon may have relatively little applicability in the civilian economy because they "oversatisfy" civilian requirements and few people or firms are willing to pay for them. With regard to the "spillover" from NASA's R and D, the Denver Research Institute[123] concluded "that the more subtle forms of technological transfer have had, and will continue to have the greatest impact—not the direct product type of transfer which is most often publicized."

Whether or not the "spillover" will be very great, it is important that policies be carried out which will increase the "spillover," so long as their value exceeds their cost. What are some of the policies that should be studied in this regard? First, there is government patent policy, which was mentioned in the previous section. As is well known, various government agencies do not have the same policy with regard to patents resulting from R and D carried out by contractors, the most important difference for present purposes being between the DOD, which allows the contractor to have title to inventions developed as the result of government R and D, and NASA (and others), which itself takes title to such inventions.

If, as is alleged by NAM and other groups, the contractors would have a greater incentive to do the additional development and marketing required to bring the invention to the market if they had patent protection, a revision of NASA's policy might mean more "spillover" at little social cost. On the other hand, these benefits might be more than offset by the slower rate of diffusion of the invention to other members of the industry. It should be possible and worthwhile to obtain more information regarding the relative importance of these and other conflicting factors.[124,125]

Second, there are various techniques that the government might adopt to help disseminate information regarding military and space R and D results to the civilian economy. According to some observers, the DOD is particularly prone to neglect the dissemination of

---

[123] J. Weeles, L. Marts, R. Waterman, J. Gilmore and R. Venuti, *Commercial Application of Missile-Space Technology* (Denver: Denver Research Institute, 1963).

[124] Leontief, *op. cit.*

[125] Preston, *op. cit.*

information to civilian industry, in part because, unlike the AEC and NASA, this is not one of its legal functions.[126] It seems worth while to look more carefully into the cost and probable benefits to be derived from various dissemination techniques. With regard to unpublished results of R and D, a more effective index of ongoing and previous R and D projects might be worth more, in its effects on "spillover," than it would cost. Of course, there have been Congressional hearings dealing with this general subject, and individuals within NASA, CEA, Commerce, and elsewhere have been concerned with it. But I am aware of no really thorough study of this subject, although the National Planning Association has begun some detailed work on it.

Third, some of the relevant Government agencies might do more to promote their R and D results. For example, when the AEC merely released data on nuclear science and technology, little happened, the result being that it undertook to develop and promote nuclear technology itself. Perhaps some of the other agencies should do more in the way of such additional R and D and promotional work. NASA is making a number of attempts to "match up" inventions occurring as byproducts of its work with civilian industry, to call the results to the attention of industry, and to work with industry representatives. (For a brief description of these programs, see Allison.[127]) It is too early to tell how these projects—involving Midwest Research Institute, the University of Indiana, and others—will work out, but it should be possible in a few years to study the record and make at least a tentative evaluation.

THE SUPPLY OF ENGINEERS AND SCIENTISTS

Another subject that has received considerable attention in the post-Sputnik era is the supply of engineering and scientific personnel. It is often asserted that the United States is suffering from a shortage of such personnel and that the existing supply is badly allocated among alternative uses. Although considerable work remains to be done in this area, the issues seem to have been clarified considerably by the work of Blank and Stigler,[128] Alchian, Arrow, and

[126] R. Solow, "Gearing Military R and D to Economic Growth," *Harvard Business Review*, December, 1962.

[127] D. Allison, "The Civilian Technology Lag," *International Science and Technology*, December, 1963.

[128] D. Blank and G. Stigler, *The Demand and Supply of Scientific Personnel* (National Bureau of Economic Research, 1957).

Capron,[129] and others. Moreover, the National Science Foundation has provided some much-needed data.

The NSF data show that there has been a tremendous growth in the number of scientists and engineers in the United States. According to Mills,[130] there were about 45,000 in 1900, 149,000 in 1920, 378,000 in 1940, and 1,110,000 in1959. For scientists, this amounted to an average annual rate of increase of more than seven percent; for engineers, the average annual rate of increase was more than six percent. Of course, these results, as well as those given below, depend on how one defines a "scientist" or an "engineer." For Mills' definitions, see his book.[131]

Obviously, not all engineers and scientists are engaged in research and development. According to NSF data pertaining to 1960, about 43 percent of the scientists were so employed—23 percent being in production, 20 percent being in teaching, and 14 percent being in other activities. And about 30 percent of the engineers were in R and D—40 percent being in production, 2 percent being in teaching, and 28 percent being in other activities.

To what extent has there been a "shortage" of engineers and scientists? The answer is not as obvious as it may seem. As a first step, one must differentiate between several possible meanings of "shortage. First, a shortage may be defined as a situation where more scientists and engineers are demanded at going salaries than are supplied.[132] Second, a shortage may be defined as a situation where such a discrepancy between demand and supply occurs temporarily because salary adjustments lag behind a rising market demand. Third, a shortage may be defined as a situation where wages rise, with the result that some potential buyers are priced out of the market. Fourth, a shortage may be defined as a case where less scientists and engineers are available and employed than should be, according to some standard of what is best for the society.

According to Alchian, Arrow and Capron,[133] there is little evidence that a shortage in the first sense has existed, although the government

---

[129] A. Alchian, K. Arrow, and W. Capron, *An Economic Analysis of the Market for Scientists and Engineers,* (RAND Corporation, 1958).

[130] T. Mills, "National Requirements for Scientists and Engineers: A Second Illustration," *Economics of Higher Education,* 1962.

[131] *Ibid.*

[132] Brown and de Cani, *op. cit.*

[133] Alchian, Arrow, and Capron, *op. cit.*

may have used its massive buying power to depress salaries some-what. Turning to the second definition, they argue that there is considerable evidence in favor of the existence of such a shortage. Blank and Stigler,[134] who use the third definition, conclude that there is little evidence of a shortage of this sort, but Hansen[135] suggests that the more recent data do confirm its existence.

Although the most important definition is the last one, it is very difficult to determine how many scientists and engineers "should" be employed in the U.S. Comparisons are sometimes made with the Soviet Union, but it is by no means clear that we should use our resources in the same way that it does. Another criterion is to project the relationship between the numbers in these professions and output into the future. For example, the Bureau of Labor Statistics[136] recently estimated that in 1970 we would require a 90 percent increase in the number of scientists and engineers over 1959 levels, for a total of about 550,000 scientists and 1,485,000 engineers. But there is no reason to believe that this would be the optimal number, since the assumptions involved in these projections have no con-vincing theoretical basis.[137]

On the basis of the reasoning in Section 6, one would expect that there is a shortage of scientists and engineers, relative to the number that would maximize civilian production. But as we concluded there, much more work is required to determine the extent of the alleged external economies. Until this work is done, the size of this shortage must be a matter of conjecture. Finally, those charged with the responsibility for national defense may provide another definition of the number of engineers and scientists that "should" be employed. According to this criterion, it has sometimes been alleged that a "shortage" exists. Again, its size has varied, depending on whose judgment was used.

Is the existing supply of scientists and engineers allocated opti-mally among alternative uses? Particularly since the advent of the space program, there has been a feeling in many quarters that too

---

[134] Blank and Stigler, *op. cit.*

[135] W. Hansen, "The 'Shortage' of Engineers," *Review of Economics and Statistics,* 1961.

[136] National Science Foundation, *The Long-Range Demand for Scientific and Technical Personnel* (Washington, 1961).

[137] Alchian, Arrow and Capron, *op. cit.*

much of our talent was being allocated to military and space work and too little was being allocated to civilian needs. Although this question is closely tied up with the larger question of national goals, it also involves the efficiency with which the DOD and NASA use the engineers and scientists that they currently hire, directly or indirectly. In view of the lack of incentives for efficiency in CPFF contracts, it seems likely that the military and space effort uses many more engineers and scientists than in fact they require and that consequently there is some malallocation of talent.

Finally, what are some of the important areas where further research is needed? First, although there has been a considerable amount of work dealing with the choice of occupation by young people, there seems to be relatively little information regarding the effects of changes in relative salary levels on such choices. Since this is presumed to be one of the important mechanisms by which a competitive, free enterprise economy allocates manpower, it is important that we gain a better understanding of the role that salary expectations really do play in this area.

Second, it would be useful to have more information regarding the extent of the government's power to control wages paid by its contractors. It would also be useful, as noted in Section 7, if additional research were carried out to formulate contracts which would contain greater incentives for efficiency and at the same time be feasible.

THE DIFFUSION OF RESULTS OF R AND D

Another area that has attracted considerable interest is the diffusion of the results of R and D. Studies by Griliches,[138] Mansfield[139, 140, 141], and others have been concerned with the rate of diffusion and the characteristics of the firms that are technical leaders or laggards, some of the principal results being as follows: First, for new techniques there seems to be a definite "bandwagon" or "contagion"

[138] J. Griliches, "Hybrid Corn: An Exploration in the Economics of Technological Change," *Econometrics*, 1957.

[139] E. Mansfield, "Technical Change and the Rate of Imitation," *Econometrics*, 1961.

[140] E. Mansfield, "The Speed of Response of Firms to New Techniques," *Quarterly Journal of Economics*, 1963.

[141] E. Mansfield, "Intrafirm Rates of Diffusion of an Innovation," *Review of Economics and Statistics*, 1963.

effect. As the number of firms in an industry using an innovation increases, the probability of its adoption by a non-user increases as well. Second, the rate of diffusion among firms tends to be higher for more profitable innovations and for those requiring relatively small investments. The rate of diffusion also differs among industries, there being some slight indication that it is higher in less concentrated industrial categories. The relationship between these variables and the rate of diffusion is in surprisingly close accord with a simple theory of the imitation process.[142] Note that in none of the cases considered in these studies were patents a critical factor, since they were held by the equipment producers.

Third, there may be some tendency for the rate of diffusion to be higher when the innovation does not replace very durable equipment, when an industry's output is growing rapidly, and when the innovation's introduction into the industry is relatively recent. Fourth, the speed with which a particular firm begins using a new technique is directly related to the firm's size and the profitability of its investment in the technique. But a firm's rate of growth, its profit level, its liquidity, its profit trend, or the age of its management seem to have no consistent or close relationship with how soon a firm adopts an innovation.

Fifth, in most industries, only a relatively weak tendency exists for the same firms to be consistently the earliest to introduce different innovations. The leaders in the case of one innovation are quite often followers for another, especially if the innovations become available at widely different points in time. Sixth, once firms begin to use a new technique, there are significant differences in how rapidly they switch over from the old technology to the new. If the case of the diesel locomotive is at all representative, this intrafirm rate of diffusion is directly related to the profitability of the innovation to the firm, the length of time the firm waited before beginning to use the innovation, and the age distribution of the firm's old equipment.[143] Small firms, slower to begin using a new technique, tend to be somewhat quicker than large ones to substitute it for the old technique once they begin.[144]

In this field, what are some of the areas requiring further work?

[142] Mansfield, "Technical Change and Rate of Imitation," *op. cit.*
[143] Mansfield, "Intrafirm Rates of Diffusion of an Innovation," *op. cit.*
[144] *Ibid.*

First, research is needed to determine the sorts of help that can effectively be given the small firms, which tend to be the laggards in many industries. Unable to afford a large technical staff, at a disadvantage in the capital markets, unwilling to take the risks involved in introducing an innovation requiring any appreciable investment, these firms often seem to wait too long before beginning to use new techniques. The Industrial Extension Service discussed in Section 6 was designed to help cope with this problem, but whether it is the best way is by no means clear. We need more work here.

Second, more research should be conducted to devise means of breaking down other important barriers to the diffusion of innovations. The policies of various government agencies (e.g., some types of security regulations) and legal restrictions of various types (e.g., building codes) are often alleged to impede unnecessarily the diffusion of technology. The attitudes of both management and labor have constituted barriers in particular cases. Studies are needed which will point the way toward a more efficient and rapid utilization of existent technology.

Third, better theories of the diffusion process, probably making extensive use of electronic computers, must be formulated. As pointed out by the Behavioral Science Subpanel of the President's Science Advisory Committee,[145] developments to date have indicated that, if reasonably good predictions of a detailed nature are to be made, the existing, highly simplified models must be extended and more extensive data must be collected.

CONCLUSION

As can be seen from the previous sections, much of the information that is needed to guide public policy is not available; and one cannot say with any certainty that, of a number of seemingly sensible courses of action, one will be best. Unfortunately, we know relatively little about the amount that should be spent on R and D if a particular rate of economic growth is to be attained, the effects of business concentration on the amount and efficiency of R and D, the way industrial and government R and D should be managed, the extent and manner in which the government should support civilian

---

[145] Behavioral Science Subpanel, President's Science Advisory Committee, *Strengthening The Behavioral Sciences*, Washington, 1957.

technology, the extent to which our supply of engineers and scientists should be expanded, and the way in which barriers to the diffusion of technology should be broken down.

The required information is not available for two reasons. First, the relevant basic research has not been completed in many areas, because the problems involved are extremely difficult and until very recently only a very few people were concerned with them. Second, what information we do have at this point has not been brought together in a systematic and comprehensive way, and reviewed to see what implications they have for public policy toward science and technology. Although some people in the Council of Economic Advisors, the Commerce Department, and elsewhere in the Government have done what they could, their time and staff have been very limited.

Hopefully, by pointing out the areas where work is badly needed, this paper will help to stimulate economists and others to turn their attention toward these important unsolved problems. Moreover, by showing the great need for data which can only be provided by industrial laboratories and other business concerns, the paper may help to overcome the reluctance of some firms to divulge such information. The potential social payoff from research designed to close some of these current gaps in our knowledge seems to me to be very great.

PART 2
THE IMPACT OF
TECHNOLOGICAL CHANGE

Great private and Government expenditures are made on research and development to hasten technical change, presumably to benefit the firm or the economy. What is the payoff from technological change? Is its impact always beneficial? Various aspects of these questions are analyzed by the contributors in Part 2.

Richard Nelson studies the contribution of technical advance to the growth of potential output in the economy. He finds that this contribution has been underestimated by economists who have treated it as a residual after giving primary attention to other variables affecting growth. Indeed, he believes with Schumpeter that the economic growth process of advanced nations probably is best viewed with technological change in the leading role.

RICHARD R. NELSON is an economist with the Rand Corporation. He received his B.A. from Oberlin College and his Ph.D. from Yale University. He is a member of the National Inventors Council and a consultant to various government agencies. He has also served on the staff of the President's Council of Economic Advisers. He is presently writing a book on *Technological Change, Economic Growth and Public Policy*.

CHAPTER 8

TECHNICAL ADVANCE
AND GROWTH OF
POTENTIAL OUTPUT

Richard R. Nelson

In this paper I shall discuss some of the things that economists know, and don't know, about the role of technical advance in increasing the potential output of the economy. By potential output I mean the output of want satisfying goods and services the economy is capable of producing at high levels of employment and utilization of the capital stock.

Notice that I am talking about potential output—the ability to produce goods and services—not actual output. The two can differ and markedly, their difference being reflected in the unemployment rate. I shall not be concerned in this paper with any effects technical advance may have on the tendencies of the economy toward unemployment or inflation. However, I shall say flatly here that there is little evidence that the problems of maintaining full employment in the face of rapid technical change are much, if any, more difficult than the problems of maintaining full employment when technical change is more leisurely. But this is a topic of a different paper.

THE DETERMINANTS OF POTENTIAL OUTPUT AND ITS GROWTH

Given the number of people able and willing to work, the potential output of an economy—its ability to meet wants—is constrained by the quantities of different kinds of goods and services that can be

143

produced per worker. The state of technical knowledge is one of the principal determinants of potential output per worker, but of course, there are others as well. In addition to the level of technical knowledge, output per worker depends mainly upon: (1) the education, skill, experience, health, and length and intensity of effort of workers; (2) the amount and vintages of machines, factory buildings, trucks, warehouses and other producers plant and equipment, and the stock of public capital such as roads, water systems, school buildings and hospitals; (3) the availability of natural resources; and (4) the rules of the game—the system of incentives and constraints which confronts individual producing and decision-making units. This vital catch-all variable encompasses such factors as the size of markets, the scope and effectiveness of public policy, and the stability of institutions.

These determinants are, of course, constraints. Within the limits set by these constraints, and given time for resources to be reallocated, there is considerable range for public and private choice with respect to what and how much can be produced. The most dramatic evidence of the range of choice has been provided during periods of mobilization and demobilization during which the output mix changed dramatically and over relatively short periods of time. Society presently has a choice of how much of its productive potential to allocate to meeting defense needs, building roads, producing food, or teaching children.

Thus potential output must be defined as a range of possibilities; the outer boundary or frontier of the set of output possibilities open to society over a period of time. Growth of potential output is a shifting outward of this frontier; an enlargement in the set of the possible. In this paper I am interested principally in potential output per capita. Growth of potential output per capita generally requires either increased economic participation and effort per capita, or investment to expand or improve the basic determinants. In the past there has been a tendency for the intensity of economic effort to decrease—through shorter work weeks, longer vacations, earlier retirements—rather than increase. The principal price of growth has been investment—the allocation of human and material resources to building future economic capability rather than to present consumption uses.

Let us use GNP as a rough index of output potential.[1] Between 1920 and 1960 real GNP more than tripled and real GNP per worker and per person roughly doubled. This impressive growth of output per worker despite a significant decline in the length of the average work week, has been due largely to investment—in expanding or improving the stock of producers plant and equipment and of public overhead capital, in increasing and improving the skills of the labor force, and in increasing technical knowledge. Since 1920 the American economy has annually devoted roughly one-third of its resources to these purposes. Much of this investment has been for replacement purposes or for equipping new workers, but much of it has represented an increase in the amount of production resources available to the average worker. The capital stock, educational attainment, and technological knowledge have advanced, together and greatly.

How important has technical change been relative to the other basic factors? In order to provide a feel for the answer to this question, I shall first survey a class of studies which have attempted to provide an answer, and then criticize them.

Denison-Solow Type Models

In recent years there have been a number of studies which have attempted to isolate and measure the relative contributions of the different forms of investment and the other factors that have increased output potential. The most influential have been various studies by Denison[2] and Solow,[3] but almost all of the studies have followed a similar methodology and have arrived at similar results.

There are three key elements to the general art form. First, as I have been doing above, growth of Gross National Product, usually adjusted to take account of changes in the unemployment rate, is used as an index of the rate of growth of output potential. Second, the formal analysis is built around the effects of growing capital stock, average educational attainments, and sometimes a few other

---

[1] I shall discuss the problems and biases in using growth of GNP as an index of growth of potential output later.

[2] E. F. Denison, *The Sources of Economic Growth in the United States and the Alternatives Before Us.* Committee on Economic Development, 1962.

[3] R. M. Solow, "Technical Change and the Aggregate Production Function," *Review of Economics and Statistics,* August, 1957.

variables, on the growth of output per worker or per manhour with technical progress being treated as a court of last result—that is, brought in as a residual or as a time trend to account for the remaining growth unexplained by the factors treated explicitly. Third, with some important exceptions that I shall discuss shortly, the factors affecting growth are treated as independent, both in their magnitude and their effect.

The discussion I present below follows precisely none of the studies that fit this art form but draws on several of them and is in the spirit of most of them.

Table 8–1 presents data on the growth of potential GNP over the

TABLE 8-1

AVERAGE ANNUAL PERCENTAGE RATES OF CHANGE

	Potential GNP	Labor	Output per Worker
1920–1929	4.0	1.6	2.4
1929–1947	2.5	1.3	1.2
1947–1960	4.0	1.3	2.7
1920–1960	3.3	1.4	1.9

SOURCE: R. R. Nelson, "Aggregate Production Functions and Medium Range Growth Projections," *American Economic Review*, September, 1964.

1920–60 period, the raw data in this kind of analysis. The series is based on the actual GNP series, deflated for price changes and adjusted to take account of varying unemployment rates. Table 8–1 shows that more than half of the growth of output over the GNP period has been the result of growth of output per worker, rather than growth of the labor force, and further, that productivity growth has been much more variable than labor force growth.

Table 8–2 presents data on the growth of capital per worker (measured by the price deflated valued private structures and equipment other than farm residences) and relates that series to the growth of output per worker series from Table 8–1.

Table 8–2 shows that changes in the rate of growth of physical capital per worker have been strongly associated with changes in the rate of growth output per worker. But how much of the increase in output per worker can growing capital intensity explain? Various analyses and studies suggest that it takes roughly a two to four percent increase in capital per worker to increase output per worker by one percent.[4] If this is the case, the growth of capital per worker shown in Table 8–2 can explain roughly one-third to one-sixth of the growth of output per worker, but not more.

TABLE 8–2

ANNUAL PERCENTAGE RATES OF GROWTH

	Output per Worker	Capital per Worker
1920–1929	2.4	2.4
1929–1947	1.2	−.3
1947–1960	2.7	2.6
1920–1960	1.9	1.4

SOURCE: E. F. Denison, *The Sources of Economic Growth in the United States and the Alternatives Before Us*. Committee on Economic Development, 1962.

Almost all of the studies in the group I am describing treat the effect of growing capital stock of given quality in roughly the way described above. With respect to other factors that have contributed to productivity growth there is more diversity.

I shall follow Denison in his treatment of the effect of rising educational attainments. Denison bases his calculations on data which show the relationship between average years of educational attainment of a worker and his average yearly wage and salary income. (Table 8–3) Roughly speaking, the data in Table 8–3 are compatible with the rule of thumb—each increased year of educational attainment is associated with a ten percent increase in average income. But association is far from causation. Educational attain-

TABLE 8–3

Years of Education	Average Wage and Salary Income as Percent of Income of Person with an Eighth Grade Education
0	50
1–4	65
5–7	70
8	100
9–11	115
12	140
13–15	165
16 and more	235

SOURCE: E. F. Denison, *The Sources of Economic Growth in the United States and the Alternatives before Us*. Committee on Economic Development, 1962.

---

[4] The use of capital's share of GNP as a measure of the logarithmic sensitivity of output with respect to growth of capital, holding labor constraint, leads to the four percent figure. Regression analysis tends to yield an estimate of three percent or somewhat lower.

ment appears to be associated with greater ability or energy and a family background of relatively high income which would themselves have led to higher than average earnings even in the absence of higher education. Denison assumes that three-fifths of the increases in income associated with each additional year of education is due to that year rather than to these other characteristics of educated people.

Over the 1920–1960 period both the average number of years of schooling and the average number of school days per year increased at a relatively steady rate; Denison assumes that the result was equivalent to an increase in average educational attainment of slightly under two school years of normalized length per decade. Under Denison's assumptions the effect of this rise would have accounted for roughly a ten percent growth per decade in average wage and salary income per worker.[5] Since wage and salary income per worker is about 70 percent of output per worker, the effect on productivity would have been seven percent a decade or about .7 percent per year. This is about 35 to 40 percent of the average yearly growth in productivity. While other treatments of the contribution of rising educational attainments differ somewhat from Denison's, they all arrive at roughly similar conclusions. If the effects of measuring capital per worker and rising educational attainments are aggregated, together they account for between one-half and three-fourths of the yearly growth of labor productivity.

Several of these studies go on to examine the effect of other factors. During this period there have been significant declines in the length of the average work week and various studies have made different assumptions about the effect of this on output per worker. The size of the economy expanded greatly and there have been several estimates made of the possible impact of economies of scale. Resources have shifted from uses where they had low productivity to industries where their productivity was higher—the shift from agriculture to industry is only one example. Massell[6] has estimated that the impact of these shifts on average productivity has been substantial.

As I pointed out earlier, in most of these studies the unexplained residual is treated as a measure of the contribution of technical advance. It is not useful here to review the quantitative conclusions

---

[5] Denison's calculations are slightly different but they amount to the same thing.

[6] B. F. Massell, "A Disaggregated View of Technical Change," *Journal of Political Economy*, December, 1961.

reached by different studies. Suffice it to say that when the effect of other factors' contributions to growth are added to the effects of capital and education, naturally the unexplained residual is further reduced. In the early study of Solow which dealt only with the effect of capital, the residual was more than 80 percent of the growth of output per worker.[7] In the more recent studies, which have looked at many factors, the residual, of course, has been much smaller. Denison, for example, has a 36 percent residual. Reflecting this, the weight economists have rested on technical change in the growth process appears to have sharply diminished.

Obviously the results of such studies should be viewed with considerable caution. Many factors that have affected growth of productivity are not treated at all, and for many that are treated, it is hard to provide a measure of their effect in which any real confidence can be rested. But despite these difficulties the studies clearly push forward understanding of the growth process and our ability to develop growth policies. The examination of the contribution of other factors certainly helps to put the contribution of technical advance in perspective.

However, I believe it is dead wrong to treat the residual calculated by these studies as an index of the importance of technical advance. My criticism of the tendency to do this goes deeper than concern about the accuracy with which the contributions of other factors are estimated. I think it wrong for two basic reasons. First, examination of the wide variety of interactions involved in the economic growth process suggests that the rate and direction of technical progress is a major factor determining the quantity and effect (as measured by a Denison type analysis) of other forms of investment. Second, the use of potential GNP as a measure of the growth of output potential has a great number of difficulties and, in particular, tends to miss some of the most important contributions of technical advance.

INTERACTIONS IN THE GROWTH PROCESS AND THE CATALYTIC ROLE OF TECHNOLOGICAL CHANGE

While the separate identification approach of the models I have just described yields many important insights, it misses a lot that is extremely important. In particular, by abstracting from the interde-

---

[7] In terms of explanation of changes in output per man hour the residual was even larger.

pendencies between the different factors that contribute to growth, it tends to underestimate significantly the sensitivity of the growth rate to changes in any one of them.

One of the important interdependencies has been treated by Robert Solow.[8] He has pointed out that to the extent that new technology needs to be embodied in new capital, the rate of investment in plant and equipment is a strong factor in determining the extent to which the average technique in use lags behind the most advanced technology. An acceleration of growth of the capital stock results not only in an increase in the rate of growth of capital per worker, but also in a decline in the average age of capital.

In addition, Schmookler[9] has shown that rapid growth in the capital stock stimulates design improvements. A high rate of investment means a high potential market for inventions which require embodiment. Further, it is clear that the early versions of a new product of process are likely to be quite primitive and plagued by unforeseen difficulties. Improvement and perfection is a sequential learning process. The rate of learning is dependent not only upon the length of experience with a particular version of the technology, but on the ability to actually try suggested improvements. If these improvements require embodiment, the rate of learning will be strongly affected by the rate of new investment. This complementarity between learning and investment implies that rapid rate of growth of capital not only keeps the technology in use close to the frontier, but also helps to accelerate the rate at which the frontier advances.[10]

However, if investment in plant and equipment stimulates technological advance, the favor is quite amply returned. Investment booms often are the result of the development of new products. The rate of technological progress clearly is a major factor determining the profitability of investing in new equipment. At a constant level of

---

[8] R. M. Solow, "Investment and Technical Change" in *Mathematical Methods in the Social Sciences* (Stanford: Stanford University Press, 1959).

[9] J. Schmookler, "Determinants of Industrial Invention" in *The Rate and Direction of Inventive Activity* (Princeton: Princeton University Press, 1962).

[10] As Dension has observed, however, the complementarity effects of new investment are probably subject to rather sharply diminishing returns. Only a limited amount of new capital is needed to embody new technology and to permit experimentation and experience with new techniques. Certainly not very much new capital is needed to take care of moderate shifts in labor allocation.

technology expansion of the capital stock would shortly be deterred by sharply diminishing returns. After a point, equipping a worker with a larger or sturdier shovel will fail to raise his output by very much. But the invention of a ditch-digging machine or bulldozer allows each worker to use a great deal more capital. Thus, not only is it true that had capital growth been slower, technical progress would have been slower. It also is true that had technical progress been slower, the rate of growth of physical capital and the impact upon productivity of that growth would have been much smaller.

Technical advance and education also are linked in a number of ways. In recent years, at least, the rate of increase in technological understanding has been closely related to the number of educated people engaged in R&D. Further, industries and firms which have large research and development staffs also tend to employ a relatively high percentage of scientists, engineers, technicians, and other professionally-trained people in management, sales and production positions. This is scarcely surprising. Technologically progressive firms need management people who can evaluate and perceive the nature of their potential market. New product information must be communicated from the developing firm to this potential market by salesmen who can describe the product and its uses and can answer questions. In the early stages of production before the techniques become routinized, highly trained people are required to deal with the problems which invariably arise. Thus the ability of the economy to generate and benefit from technological change is a function of how much we have invested in education.

But in turn the remunerativeness of education and the ability of the economy to absorb an increasing proportion of educated people is due in large part to technological advance. Obviously the salaries of research and development scientists and engineers is a reflection of the returns to the technological advances their work leads to. Indeed the demand for and economic return to educated people generally (not just R&D scientists and engineers) may be primarily determined by the desired and actual rate of technological advance. The high returns to a chemical engineer in the production force working with a new chemical process is due to the fact that the process is sufficiently new so that it cannot be routinized for less highly trained labor. The relatively high remuneration of trained management, sales and production people reflect their ability to deal expertly and imaginatively with problems created by new products and techniques and other environmental changes. The economic advantage of education to people in these positions extends far beyond the imparting of specific skills to deal with specific problems. It also lies in the added flexibility, the added ability to learn new things and to deal with new kinds of problems that some types of education impart and which rapid technological change makes important.

Thus if we consider the three principal forms of investment—physical capital, education, and technological advance—it is clear that increases in one tend to stimulate increased returns to and increased quantities of the other. The three forms of investment interact so strongly that it becomes somewhat dubious to cast any one of them in the star's role and view the other two as merely supporting cast. However, if one character must be given the star's billing in the drama of economic growth, I believe that technological advance fits the bill best.

In countries like the United States the capital stock, levels of education and institutions historically have evolved along with advances in knowledge. In such societies, the growth process is best understood as revolving around technological change. This choice of perspective seems the most fruitful for analyzing changes in the magnitude and direction of economic activity. An advance here is more likely to energize the rest of the system than an equivalent act of investment in education or physical capital. (Which does not imply that the social rate of return, as conventionally measured, is higher on R&D than on other types of investment.) It may be a different matter for those underdeveloped countries which can borrow technology; there capital formation and education may have the most powerful thrust. But I believe with Schumpeter that the economic growth process of advanced nations probably is best viewed with technological change in the leading role, and capital formation and education playing the role of necessary supports.

NEW PRODUCTS AND ECONOMIC GROWTH

A second reason why I feel that the models described earlier do not provide an adequate feel for the importance of technological progress in the growth process rests on the failure of growth of potential GNP to measure adequately some important aspects of growth of output potential. GNP presently provides the best single available number to summarize output performance.[11] But it has some serious weaknesses, particularly for measuring long run changes. In particular, the GNP measure tends to be most inadequate where technological change is most important—when new final products are introduced to the economy. Denison's attribution of two-thirds of growth of GNP to causes other than technological advance, even if true, would still be pallid.

Technological advances can be process changes which increase the ability of the economy to produce established private or public consumption goods. Or they can be product advances that create the possibility of producing substantially new or improved consumption goods. The automatic loom and the improved catalytic process equipment for producing gasoline were process changes. They involved new machinery, but did not expand the range of consumption goods. Both increased the potential of the economy to produce existing final products, but did not introduce any new dimension to the set of goods which determine the welfare of consumers. On the other hand, the development of the airplane, penicillin, and television did expand the range of final goods and services.[12] They permitted us to satisfy wants which could not be satisfied before.

The differentiation between process and product is not razor sharp. Final products are after all processes for satisfying consumer wants. In many uses new final goods are simply more efficient processes—less costly ways of meeting needs that were met before. In other instances there is a difference in kind. Wants which could not be appeased by older goods and services are satisfied. While in some situations the airplane is simply a less costly way to travel (counting time) than a train, prior to the modern airplane it was impossible to travel across the country in less than two days, much less five hours; not more difficult or expensive—impossible. Penicillin

---

[11] Gross National Product in any year is (roughly speaking) the sum of the goods and services purchased by consumers, provided by governments, or purchased by business firms to increase their productive capacity. The output of goods which are sold on the market is valued at market prices; those goods (like defense and public education) which are not provided to the public through market channels are valued at cost.

[12] By the introduction of a new final good I mean the introduction of a new good for which no combination of older goods provides a perfect substitute.

has made it possible—not just less costly—to save the lives of many people with certain infections.

When technological advance increases productivity in the production of existing goods and services, its contribution is not essentially different from that of any other investment. For enlarging the spectrum of choice, however, there is no perfect substitute for investment in advancing technology. The dramatic increase in standards of health we have achieved could not have been achieved simply by allocating more men and equipment to meeting health needs. This has happened but the main factor which has permitted the improvement has been advance in the quality of medicines and medical practice. The improvements in transportation and communications services that we have achieved likewise would have been impossible but for the invention and development of the radio and the airplane. And these and other new goods represent the most treasured prizes of economic growth.

Growth of economic potential has a direction as well as a rate. If the production possibilities frontier shifted out uniformly there would be little difficulty in providing a scalar measure of growth, and indeed potential GNP as it is calculated would provide a good measure. However, a more productive process for making aluminum will not result in a uniform shifting out of the frontier; rather it will shift out those points on the frontier which involve a large aluminum output more than it will shift our other points. And the creation of a new final product will actually introduce a new dimension to production possibilities. This is the sine qua non of non-uniform growths. And the GNP series measures very inadequately with growth of this kind.

Without new products, Americans still would have achieved a very significant increase in their standard of living. But the kinds of improvements would have been different. And the fourfold increase in GNP since 1900 would have meant far less in terms of potential to meet wants. New products are measured in the GNP calculations by the amount people spent on them, but for many people the value of being able to obtain the new product far exceeds the total price they pay. If airplane service were eliminated from the spectrum of final products, many consumers would require a significant increment of income to achieve comparable levels of satisfaction. For those for whom penicillin is the only thing that blocks death, the value of the new product clearly is not measurable.[13]

Put another way, the consumer price index suggests that the prices of consumer goods and services in 1960 were approximately three times the 1900 level. But it is probable that most people would be willing to settle for far less than three dollars to spend on goods available in 1960 at 1960 prices rather than one dollar to spend on goods available in 1900 at 1900 prices.[14] But it is impossible to say how much less.

In summary, it is clear that we have no single satisfactory measure of the growth of potential experienced since 1900; even conceptually no scalar member would be applicable. Our growth of potential has involved at least four aspects; a growth of capability for producing old goods and services given the amount of labor we have dedicated to economic activity (for which growth of GNP may be an approximate measure); a 25 percent reduction in the average work week, a reduction in the burdensomeness of labor, and an enrichment in the kinds of products and services the economy can provide.

The aspects of economic growth not adequately measured by GNP loom the largest. And many of these are benefits which are largely attributable to technological advance rather than to generalized economic growth. The fact of measured economic growth is that real GNP per person is more than twice as large as in 1900. But it is far more important that technological change has so altered the nature of society and the quality of life as to make GNP comparisons over such long periods of time meaningless. Man today has a life expectancy of 70 years, is rather adequately protected from a wide range of

---

[13] I am not arguing here that, because of the introduction of new products, growth of GNP underestimates growth of welfare. Rather, I am arguing that a given growth of measured GNP means more in terms of consumer satisfaction if it is accompanied by the availability of new products than if it is not. As Marshall and later Hicks pointed out long ago, if we forbid a person from buying any of a particular product he presently is purchasing, he is made worse off even if he can spend the money saved in other products at existing prices. The agreement is reversible. People with a given amount of money income and given and fixed product prices will be made better off if a new product is introduced to their choice set—provided the product and its price are sufficiently attractive so that they buy some of it.

[14] Some people would not. A 1960 dollar buys far less personal service and housing space than did a 1900 dollar. For those whose tastes stress these things, it is possible that they would be willing to trade much more than three 1960 dollars for one 1900 dollar and the accompanying prices.

devastating diseases, has teeth extracted with relatively little pain, is shielded from heat by air-conditioning and the cold by central heating, has his range of diversions and opportunities for mental liberation increased by television, movies, and mass-produced newspapers and books, and his view of the world altered by the opportunities for cheap and rapid travel by autos and airplanes.

Even without these developments, a near tripling of GNP per person would have been a boon helping to eradicate poverty and increase the pleasurableness of life. But it would have been far less powerful a liberating force if we had been restricted to the consumption possibilities of 1900—wider carriages, more coal for the kitchen stove, and more kerosene for the oil lamp. This is the point the studies above miss. But it is the heart of the matter.

In addition to the macroeconomic impact of technological change as discussed by Nelson, there is a microeconomic impact, i.e., on the firm. Sociologist Moore analyzes the effect of technological change on industrial organization. First considering technological change as an independent variable, Moore analyzes its influence on occupational structure, man-machine relations, the demand for experts, and managerial tasks. Then considering technological change as a dependent variable, he discusses the impact of the organization on the production of technology.

WILBERT E. MOORE is a Sociologist, Russell Sage Foundation, and Visiting Professor in Sociology at Princeton University. He attended Linfield College for his B.A. degree, the University of Oregon for his M.A., and received his Ph.D. from Harvard. He is also president of the American Sociological Association. His published works include: *Economic Demography of Eastern and Southern Europe, Industrial Relations and the Social Order, Industrialization and Labor, Economy and Society, The Conduct of the Corporation, Man, Time, and Society, Social Change,* and *The Impact of Industry.*

CHAPTER 9

THE IMPACT OF TECHNOLOGICAL CHANGE ON INDUSTRIAL ORGANIZATION[1]

Wilbert E. Moore

There is a very popular notion abroad in the land that technology is an automatic, autonomous, and indeed sovereign source of social change. This idea is, of course, much admired by technologists, for after all that makes them leaders, but it will not pass muster as a social theory. To a remarkable degree, in the modern world every economy or society gets about the technology that it deserves, or at least what it is able and willing to support. But I have also previously argued[2] that each stage of economic development gets about the kind of organizational theory that it deserves, as sensible administrative policies vary not only with the state of technology but also with the qualities of the inhabitants of administrative organizations.

These caveats are relevant to my task here, for although I shall start by considering technology as an independent variable that has important and specifiable consequences for the character of industrial organization, I shall conclude by turning the relationship about,

---

[1] W. E. Moore, "Technological Change and Industrial Organization," in International Social Science Council, *Social Implications of Technological Change*, Paris: 1962, pp. 199–209. In the present effort I shall be repeating some points expressed there, but here I give greater attention to the interplay between productive technology and administrative technology, and take a closer look at technology as a dependent variable, that is, as useful innovations often created within the industrial organizations themselves.

[2] *Ibid.*, pp. 207–209.

and briefly consider industrial organization as a source of technological change. For the sake of clarity it should be noted that by industrial organization I shall mean the networks of positions and roles, the goals and rules of conduct comprising productive units. The term is thus approximately equivalent to the firm in an enterprise economy, with somewhat more difficult but not impossible identification of comparable units in socialist and communist states. I am not concerned here with the effect of technology on the allocation of other factors of production or on the competitive position of firms, industries, or sectors of the economy. For this range of problems I regard the term "industrial organization" as ambiguous and improper.

TECHNOLOGICAL CHANGE AS AN INDEPENDENT VARIABLE

The most conspicuous consequences of technological change for industrial organizations are to be found in their general "shape," as reflected for example in the numerical distribution of various skills and responsibilities, and in critical dimensions of internal relationships such as the interaction of men and machines and the ways in which expert information flows and authority is exercised.

Changes in Occupational Structure

Successive improvement in man's attempt to adjust to his environment and extend his mastery over it give substance to conceptions of social evolution as comprising *part* of the changeful qualities of social life. In an industrial economy technological change is exceptionally rapid, being both organized and institutionalized, and thus deliberate in high degree. Its impact on the allocation of productive tasks, that is, occupations, is multiple and, from an evaluative point of view, mixed. Negatively, technological change often results in breaking up of skill combinations, which we may call skill dilution, and outright skill obsolescence. Though the distinction is not always clear in practice, skill dilution is most commonly attributable to changes in productive processes, and skill obsolescence to changes, and especially to substitutions, in industrial products. Less noticed by social critics but of crucial importance in industrial evolution is a third change in occupational demand, which is the need for new skills and new skill combinations, which results generally in occupational upgrading.

Since technology itself is highly diverse, and since the "latest" technology may not be instantaneously and generally adopted, all of these processes may be going on simultaneously. Certainly, the overriding long-term trend has been that of upgrading, with well-known human costs for those left behind in the transformation.[3] Within industrial organization this process is reflected in the proportional shifts of production workers from the unskilled to the semi-skilled and skilled; shifts from blue-collar to white-collar positions, and from supervisory to technical personnel. The geometric shape of the organizations comes more nearly to represent a diamond sitting on its point than a pyramid sitting on a broad base, and with lateral diversification growing relatively to vertical distinctions of skill and administrative power.

As we all now know, it is not just the men at the machines and benches that are threatened with technological displacement or challenged to acquire needful new skills. Automation and computerization threaten the job security of clerical workers and even junior managers, while demanding new design and maintenance services of a high order of trained competence.

We are, in my opinion, far from the automatic factory for most industrial processes. The machines are not self-designing, self-reproducing, self-installing, or self-maintaining. But as we move somewhat closer to the factory without workers, we should speculate a bit on the possible implications of continuous operation for the possible needs for expansion of technical personnel and possibly even for increase of policy-level executives.

Changes in Man-Machine Relations

Early forms of industrial technology made overt the subservience of the production worker to the machine in terms of both task and temporal rhythm. Subsequent developments in task subdivision and in more sophisticated machines and sequential flows of materials (and therefore sequential dependence of workers on their produc-

---

[3] Wilbert E. Moore, "Changes in Occupational Structures," in Neil J. Smelser and Seymour Martin Lipset (eds.), *Social Structure and Social Mobility in Economic Growth* (forthcoming).

tive predecessors) heightened the seeming servitude to the machine. Still later changes in productive processes have substituted mechanical for muscular work, and in the course of those changes have restored the remaining workers to machine mastery. In many industrial situations the worker now manipulates the machine, with an impressive level of what one is tempted to call dexterity, or monitors a control panel with perhaps little manual manipulation but a high requirement of responsibility.

Note that this sequence of changing relations of men and machines was not solely a result of changing technology in the narrow sense of applications of physical and chemical principles to practical uses. Machine technology and what we may call administrative technology have been interdependent all along. The social technology of wage employment, organizational design, task allocation, temporal coordination, and administrative decision and discipline antedated the technology of machine-pacing. Industrial discipline and task specialization have made possible the development of mechanical substitutes for mechanized men. Technologists in the narrow sense have often responded, sometimes tardily, to cues given by organizational planners, aided and abetted by such expert advisers as cost accountants.

Meanwhile, the organization of the work place in a highly mechanized operation bears little resemblance to the factories of our common experience or to the factories comprised of work teams and their informal relations so extensively documented in the literature of industrial sociology. For the remaining workmen, the physical setting of work is often socially sterile. The cost of achieving machine mastery is the loss of human contact, except during rest periods or out of hours. Yet the manipulator of the machine and certainly the maintenance man becomes a problem-solver and not an automaton.

The problems indeed, may become so complex that a new wave of higher-level specialization is likely to set in, with diagnosticians and varieties of therapists necessary to deal with the mechanical ills of the new technology. Note that the men manipulating and monitoring the machine, and also their supervisors and higher management, may not fully understand the processes involved. They can appraise results but not procedures, for in effect they are dealing with experts at one remove by dealing with the products of the experts' creation.

Changes in the Demand for Experts

This brings us to the growing demand for a battery of experts in the administrative operation of industrial organizations. At a minimum, experts serve as suppliers of current information on technical developments. By one view, even the hardware scientists and technicians in research and development units have chiefly a defensive function, that of alerting policy-forming executives of possibly significant external developments. As an overall view, this cynical interpretation suffers the same fatal, logical defect as the explanation of social conformity solely in terms of the expectations of others. In the present context, the defensive view would not account for the actual rate of technical innovation. That rate, within any industrial sector, is likely to be approximately proportional to the size of firm. In some fields without a highly developed theoretical system and corresponding scale of technical exellence—chemistry is a good example—the rate of innovation may be closely proportional to the man-hours of research time expended.

In the nature of the case, experts must face "outward" and be in close contact with their own professional peers, and in many cases must also represent various external clienteles within corporate councils. The latter is especially the case of the multiplying "relations specialists," the external relations include law and marketing, for example, as well as dealing with labor and cultivating a public image. Both the peer identity and the representation of clienteles introduce necessarily diverse and rather commonly discordant notes into the symphony of organizational kinship and loyalty. This probability gives rise to managerial problems that I shall note in a few moments.

The increasingly technical character of everything from metallurgy to accounting and investment means a great "technification" of managerial organization taken as a whole, and helps account for the proportional increase of "staff" positions relative to "line" positions. The burden this places on central administration is a further problem to which I now turn.

Changes in Managerial Tasks

Time was that there was a normal presumption that the various levels of management corresponded to degrees of competence on a single scale, the higher-level executives being in their lofty positions as a result of competitive selection and accumulated experience. Though the manager as a generalist is still a widely shared conviction and a goal of selection and various attempts at advanced training both in the corporation and in the academy, it is becoming increasingly difficult to maintain. It has to be recognized, at the very least, that the manager is not the fount of wisdom and technical knowledge for his subordinates. Often the reverse is true. The manager becomes the coordinator of experts, each of whom is likely to outrank his superior in specialized knowledge in his own field. Such a situation distinctly damages the cherished stereotype of the executive as a leader of men, an innovator, and a kind of exemplar of energetic virtue. Energetic and virtuous the manager or executive may be, and even, within narrow limits an innovator, but he can scarcely lead in the sense of instruction and example. Whom could he fool?

Note that these developments radically change the managerial role, but they scarcely make it simpler or even degrade it. The manager's tasks now prominently include a cultivated ability to comprehend the information and advice that stem from basic knowledge and procedures that he could not duplicate. And since the experts represent *different* bodies of knowledge and technique, there is no reason to suppose that they will speak with a single voice. They may all try to talk at once, true enough, but that scarcely qualifies for the phrase "in unison." There is indeed a notable tendency for the expert on industrial payrolls not only to welcome the request that he be practical, but to insist on it. The difficulty is that as many solutions to problems will be offered as there are experts consulted. The manager's task in dealing with experts is simply to make simultaneous sense out of discordant and contradictory advice. At the same time, of course, he must attend to all of his other responsibilities and accountabilities as a representative of his superiors, or, if he is high enough in rank, his directors and various clienteles and publics, and to a myriad of organizational controls and pressures.

Although I cannot demonstrate the point conclusively, I think the technical and deliberately changeful environment in which the modern manager operates has as a minimum effect a steady decrease in reliance on experience and precedent for current decision. The injunction to "find the better way" tends to operate more and more pervasively.

In my book on *The Conduct of the Corporation*[4] I have written disparagingly of the pretensions to professionalism on the part of business managers: ". . . Until there is established a body of abstract principles capable of application in a wide variety of situations, and until training in these principles readily distinguishes the true professional from the amateur or the man qualified only by a limited range of experience that he cannot generalize, the attempt to 'professionalize' management must be regarded as rather incomplete."[5] I also noted the virtual absence of ". . . a binding code of ethics, protective of both professional standards and of clients, and enforced chiefly by the professional body itself."

In the short time since those views were written there has not been sufficient change in the great world of corporate management to force a radical revision of my views. I think careful and weighty attention should be given, however, to such hopeful signs as the questioning or abandonment of the case method of business-school instruction, the increasing frequency of mid-career advanced study, and the development of training in rather elaborate rational-decision models using complex data inputs and analytic schemes for arriving at disciplined judgment. If this sort of thing goes very far, the merely experienced manager may be as technologically unemployable as some of us are beginning to feel in our own scholarly disciplines.

Diversification versus Linear Evolution

The long-term historic trends in technology can be partially cast into an evolutionary model, which allows both diversification through selective adaptation and cumulative or directional change as judged by growing mastery of the environment.

The world technological pool, however, reduces the prospects for

---

[4] Wilbert E. Moore, *The Conduct of the Corporation* (New York: Random House, 1962).

[5] *Ibid.*, p. 12.

replication of historical developments in areas now industrializing. This is a principal justification for the idea of cumulative change. The available technology might be likened to the shelf-stock in a supermarket, from which the shopper is free to choose without regard to the sequence in which the goods were acquired and displayed. Thus selectivity, eclectic combinations, and new adaptations are all possible and probable. There are, however, some structural constraints: increased power may break the machine rather than increasing its output, mass production is uneconomic without a system for mass distribution, and so on. More interesting are the sequential constraints. In newly developing areas capital is scarce and dear, and labor is cheap though inefficient. The temptation to import the latest, labor-saving technology is strong in the nationalistic environment of new nations, but time is still required to upgrade the labor force and develop industrial traditions. Thus, though the organizational evolution of modern industry as we know it may be foreshortened by benefit of exceptional effort and learning from past experience, it is not likely to be reversed. With perhaps distressing frequency the factories in developing areas are likely to resemble those in Manchester in the early nineteenth century, and with the same radical disparity between the manager and the managed—a disparity that has been reduced and made increasingly ambiguous by the sorts of changes we have been discussing. We are now confronted with the ironic fact that Marx has proved to be radically wrong on the continuing course of industrialized societies, but repeatedly reconfirmed as a correct analyst of the earliest stages of modernization.

THE PRODUCTION OF TECHNOLOGY

I now turn to technological change as a dependent variable, as the outcome of deliberate efforts at creative innovation, backed up by deliberate decisions to allocate time, talent, and money to the organized production of new knowledge.

Scientific Management versus The Management of Scientists

"Scientific management," as enunciated in the works of Frederick W. Taylor and his followers, assumed that both technical and decisional skills were exclusively managerial properties. Workers as

Taylor observed them were inexperienced and without industrial traditions and often without formal education. In Taylor's view they required close supervision, including instruction and discipline. He also assumed them to be "economic men," responsive primarily or exclusively to wage incentives. Though I have joined, if I did not help lead, a chorus of criticism of Taylor's administrative theories,[6] I now think he was essentially right for the time, technology, and labor force that he experienced. This is an example of the assertion that each stage of industrial development gets about the administrative theory that it deserves.

An upgraded and committed labor force requires more coordination than supervision. Even at the level of first-line supervisors, the foreman may be less technically qualified than his subordinates.

The introduction of technically-trained experts, and particularly of organized research, within the industrial organization brings the change in appropriate administrative styles into sharp focus.

The role of professionals in organizations is intrinsically ambiguous, as I have already noted. Relational experts are necessarily "two-faced,"[7] since they cannot represent the company to its clients without representing the clients to the company. And researchers are necessarily peer-oriented as well as somewhat organizationally responsible. This lack of total organizational commitment is a principal, though not the sole, source of line-staff conflict, which is a ubiquitous and intrinsic feature of industrial and indeed of all administrative organizations.

The organization and administration of scientific research has received considerable scholarly attention, most recently and effectively by Kornhauser and Marcson.[8] Two problems are especially worthy of comment: (1) The administrative scientist, such as the director of a research laboratory, commonly has to be a scientist in order to get his position, and steadily loses his current claims to scientific authority as he exercises administrative authority. (2) The

---

[6] Wilbert E. Moore, *Industrial Relations and the Social Order* (rev. ed.; New York: Macmillan Co., 1951), pp. 170–84. The same materials appeared in the first edition in 1946.

[7] W. E. Moore, *The Conduct of the Corporation,* previously cited chap. xiii, "Two-Faced Experts."

[8] William Kornhauser, *Scientists in Industry: Conflict and Accommodation* (Berkeley and Los Angeles: University of California Press, 1962); Simon Marcson, *The Scientist in American Industry* (New York: Harper & Row, Publishers, Inc., 1960).

conditions for creativity are still not firmly known, but two firm findings are that freedom is necessary and that peer orientations must be indulged. I should add a third view, less firmly grounded, that security of position is more conducive to creativity than is anxiety.

Problems of Communication and Implementation

The effective production of technical innovation encounters at least two pervasive problems of administrative organization, namely, communication and managerial or "line" decision.

Jargon, argots, and patois abound in industrial organizations. Thus there is a very general need for translators and interpreters if coordination is to take place, and particularly if technical innovations are to be appraised at decision-making levels. It is not surprising, therefore, that large industrial research laboratories find it advantageous to have technically-trained "salesmen," whose mission is not to deal with external customers but rather with managers of product divisions and general managers who have to be convinced that there are practical, economically advantageous opportunities in new technical developments.

Like their kind everywhere, these salesmen often do not succeed. Acceptance and implementation of an innovation in either product or process requires positive decision and positive action. The larger the organization, presumably the larger the flow of innovative suggestions from the legitimate trouble-makers, and, I fear, the larger the number of company officers who have and often exercise veto powers. Those line officers above the potential innovator in relative rank are legitimately empowered nay-sayers, for whatever sensible, nonsensical, or merely neurotic reasons. If the decision is affirmative the innovator's path is still rough. Managers down the line, who have ordinarily not been consulted on implementation, cannot normally exercise official vetoes. Their power (though not their authority) is that of sabotage—of conscientious withholding of cooperation—and at that they are often adept.

I cannot prove it, but I firmly believe that actual product innovations, as distinct from changes in process alone, are disproportionately introduced by small and indeed often by new firms. This is their mode of entry into the market. The bureaucratization of research, if it does not destroy creativity, is likely to thwart it at the level of positive action.

Distortions of Defense

Investments of men and money in new technology are now strongly influenced by national support and in the industrial sector especially by defense spending. This means that some technologies are favored while others languish, thus again disproving merely technological primacy in social change.

The support of technology in the name of defense also means that governmental contract negotiation becomes a major managerial activity. The government, moreover, becomes the sole and insistently monopolistic customer for some technology. Changes in technology and choice of producers may be made on political as well as economic and technical grounds.

This is a major part of the contemporary production of technology. The situation affects not only industrial organization, but it also affects the way one must rationally view the relations between government and industry. The old shibboleths about keeping government out of business were tainted, and their contemporary reiteration plainly shocking. The relations between private corporations and agencies of government are multitudinous and run from cooperative interdependence to competitive or combative redefinitions of rights and responsibilities. But the ideologies of business who speak out against big government, and that includes an alarming proportion of otherwise responsible executives along with irresponsible writers of speeches and copy for institutional advertising, must speak with a forked tongue. Indeed, they must either be hypocritical or dangerously naive, knaves or fools. That is not the way the modern technological or political world is organized, or could be, and it is surely high time that a little measure of responsibility on public issues intruded itself into the thinking of the producers of technology who are also, along with the rest of us, its somewhat reluctant beneficiaries.

Maintenance of a competitive environment is a leading economic goal of the United States and one which is affected by technological change. The interactions between technological change and competition are examined by four writers.

Carl Kaysen notes that the increased importance of technical change is a major element of the "new" competition facing business managers. Since merger often appears as the most effective and economical way for the manager to meet the competition of a new product or process, Kaysen focusses on the anti-merger aspect of anti-trust policy as a test of the whole policy of regulation of competition. He indicates criteria that may be useful in regulating the "New" competition.

CARL KAYSEN is Professor of Economics at Harvard University and Associate Dean of the Graduate School of Public Administration. He holds an A.B. degree from the University of Pennsylvania and an M.A. and Ph.D. from Harvard University. He is a consultant to the U.S. Department of Defense and Deputy Special Assistant to the President for national security affairs. His publications include *Antitrust Policy*, written with Donald Turner.

CHAPTER 10

THE NEW COMPETITION AND
THE OLD REGULATION

Carl Kaysen

INTRODUCTION

Antitrust policy has long held an important role in the array of legal and institutional controls which guide and shape the functioning of markets in our economy; increasingly its place has become a central one. It is therefore appropriate that a symposium on Modern Competition should include some consideration of the impact of antitrust law and policy on the character of competition as it reflects the evolving features of modern markets.

We can single out three inter-related features as characterizing the "new competition" in the writings of those who have seen a sharp change in the nature of market competition in recent years, say the two postwar decades.[1] First is the increased importance of technical change, and competition between new and old products, or among various new products, as over against competition among standard products, or somewhat differentiated, but closely similar products. This change is in turn linked to the dramatic increase in business and total spending on research and development in this period. The evolution of the so-called ethical drug industry since the end of World War II is often quoted as an example in this respect.[2] Second

---

[1] A. D. H. Kaplan and A. E. Kahn, *Big Enterprise in a Competitive System* (Washington, D.C.: Brookings Institution, 1954); Lilienthal, *Big Business: A New Era* (New York: Pocket Books, Inc., 1953); J. K. Galbraith, *American Capitalism: The Concept of Countervailing Power* (Boston: Houghton, Mifflin Co., 1956).

[2] Presentations of the Pharmaceutical Manufacturers Association to the Kefauver Committee investigating administered prices in the drug industry. *Hearings on Administered Prices.* Part 19, Subcommittee on Antitrust and Monopoly, Committee on the Judiciary, U.S. Senate, 86;2 (Feb. 23, 24, April 20, 1960).

is the radical change in the character of marketing institutions for consumer goods: the growth of the supermarket, the discount house, the chain drug store. These, together with the continuing increase in consumer incomes, have stimulated rapid growth in advertising and emphasis on those elements of "packaging" in the product closely associated with advertising and selling. In many consumer goods industries, the efficient scale of marketing—including advertising and other selling efforts—appears to be far larger than the efficient scale of production. These two elements together have led, in turn, to the third, an increased emphasis on the significance of inter-industry competition relative to the "traditional" competition among firms in the same industry.

This characterization of the "new competition" makes it appropriate, in a relatively brief discussion of effects of antitrust to focus our attention on law and policy with respect to mergers: namely, the Celler-Kefauver amendment to Section 7 of the Clayton Act, passed in 1950, and its enforcement to date. From the perspective of business managers, mergers provide one of the most significant and economical methods of meeting the "new competition." Changing markets require corresponding adaptations by sellers seeking to survive and expand in them; mergers often are a preferred mode of adaptation. As a method of entering a new market, or finding an application for a technology newly developed within the firm, or acquiring mastery of a technology new to the firm which has become relevant to meeting the competition of a new product or process, the acquisition of a going business of the appropriate kind often appears the quickest and least risky, and therefore least expensive, path to the objective. The extent of legal obstacles to mergers may thus serve as an important measure of the degree to which the old regulation is adapted to the "new competition."

Further, there is an argument from the side of antitrust policy itself which justifies our selection of the antimerger law as the test of the whole policy. The control of mergers is preventive antitrust policy, and its application, even within the rather narrow scope allowed by the resources of the enforcement agencies, can have quite broad and lasting effects on the structure of markets.[3,4] By contrast, Section

---

[3] G. J. Stigler, "Mergers and Preventive Antitrust Policy," *University of Pennsylvania Law Review,* Nov. 1955; R. B. Heflebower, "Corporate Mergers: Policy and Economic Analysis," *Quarterly Journal of Economics,* Nov. 1963; C. Kaysen and

1 of the Sherman Act requires a fairly continuous policing effort, the effect of which tends to be more or less proportional to the continued level of effort, and Section 2, involving lengthy and difficult proceedings, and often requiring the undoing of what has long since been done to achieve much lasting change, is sharply limited in the breadth of its effects under present laws and enforcement policies.

In our examination of how the Celler-Kefauver amendment has been applied, it is useful to pursue the usual distinction among types of mergers: horizontal, vertical, and conglomerate. Horizontal mergers involve competitors selling in the same market. Where markets are geographically separated, the merger of firms selling in two different areas is not, strictly speaking, a horizontal merger. But in circumstances where significant elements of national market advertising are present, or where buying firms on the other side of the market (or firms supplying particularly important inputs) are national in scope, or cover both geographic markets involved, it seems reasonable to assimilate such market extension mergers to horizontal mergers. Such are the acquisitions of local milk distributors by major national firms such as National Dairy or Beatrice Foods, even though they have not previously operated in the particular local area in question.[5] Vertical mergers join customer and supplier; conglomerate mergers are those which join firms that are neither competitors nor customers-suppliers. The distinction between conglomerate and vertical mergers is relatively clearcut; that between horizontal and conglomerate depends on the breadth or narrowness with which market boundaries are drawn. On the Government's theory, which prevailed, cans and glass jars are products competing in the same market, and accordingly, Continental Can's acquisition of Hazel-Atlas was a horizontal merger. The defense took a different view, and characterized the merger as conglomerate.[6] A significant ele-

---

D. F. Turner, *Antitrust Policy, an Economic and Legal Analysis* (Cambridge: Harvard University Press, 1959), pp. 127–41.

[4] J. F. Weston, *The Role of Mergers in the Growth of Large Firms* (Berkeley: University of California Press, 1953), remains the most penetrating analysis of the effect of mergers around the turn of the century and in the 20's on market structure today.

[5] *Mergers and Superconcentration*, a Staff Report of the Select Committee on Small Business, House (Nov. 1962), Table 18. We shall draw heavily on the tabulation of mergers in this document.

[6] *U.S.* v *Continental Can*, 217 F Supp. 761 (1963) and 84 s. ct. 1738 (1964).

ment in the choice between these two views is the weight to be assigned in a particular merger to the element of potential competition, a matter which will be examined below.

Many mergers contain elements of all three categories, or at least two; indeed, this is typical of mergers in which both parties are large firms. But even so, these elements can be viewed separately, and, in many cases, one clearly is predominant in terms of such measures as sales or employment.[7]

Of the three categories, horizontal mergers are least relevant to our present concerns. A harsh rule which views as presumptively illegal even relatively small horizontal mergers—say, for example, those involving firms which together account for 10% of the market[8]—would in general not prevent adjustment to the kinds of competitive changes discussed above, as characteristic of the "new competition."[9] Vertical mergers are more relevant, but it is primarily conglomerate mergers, with their relation to the problems of changing technologies and inter-industry competition which are at the center of interest. Accordingly, we will examine the impact of policy and law in this area, as shown both by the mergers which the two enforcing agencies—the Anti-Trust Division of the Department of Justice and the Federal Trade Commission—have sought to prevent, and the dispositions which the courts have made of these cases. Our argument follows a threefold division: we examine the statistical pattern of cases initiated, in terms of both the total numbers of mergers and the categories defined above; then we consider the outcome of some particularly important cases; and finally we specu-

---

[7] Brown Shoe's acquisition of Kinney contained both horizontal and vertical elements. *Brown Shoe Co.* v *U.S.*, 370 US 294. Bethlehem's proposed acquisition of Youngstown was largely horizontal, though there were some small vertical elements, as well as elements of market extension. *U.S.* v *Bethlehem Steel Corporation*, 168 F. Supp. 576.

[8] Stigler, *op. cit.*

[9] It is of course possible to conceive of situations in which this statement would not hold. Thus, in the context of a static market, substantial technical change which altered the efficient size of the production and marketing unit—e.g., made possible preserving what had hitherto been a perishable processed food, requiring a larger plant and permitting a wider area of distribution from each plant—might suggest mergers on a substantial scale as the most economic mode of adaptation to the new situation. But even in this rather artificial case, the relation of the social economics—the actual resources—to the private advantages to existing owners of firms of losing as little as possible of their goodwill in the process of adaptation, is unclear.

late about the possible impact of the most reasonable general rules which could be drawn from these cases.

THE NUMBER OF MERGERS AND THE LEVEL OF ENFORCEMENT

The best current record of mergers is the list published annually by the Bureau of Economics of the Federal Trade Commission. This list includes mergers noted in the business press as well as those listed by *Moody's* and *Standard Corporation Records,* which cover only the larger firms in mining and manufacturing. While the latter series goes back to 1919, the FTC totals are available only from 1951, and a breakdown of these totals by major industry group and by acquisitions of whole firms versus acquisitions of parts of firms, including subsidiaries and divisions, is available only since 1955. The most important of these figures are shown in Table 10–1.[10]

It is clear that there has been a sharp and fairly steady increase in the number of mergers over the dozen years since Section 7 was revitalized, whatever basis of measurement is used. It is worth observing, however that the level is substantially lower than that recorded for earlier periods of high merger activity: in the 1919–29 period the *Moody's* and *SCR* total for mining and manufacturing averaged 660 per year, and reached over 1000 in 1928 and over 1200 in 1929, and this level in turn was a little lower than the peak of the merger wave at the turn of the century, which occurred in 1899.[11]

Aggregate counts of mergers, while of obvious interest, are too crude for our purposes; ideally, we would like this data classified by

---

[10] These tables are derived from the annual releases of the FTC on the number of mergers in the previous year. See in particular the releases of 22 April 64, 8 Feb. 63, 28 Jan. 62, 7 Feb. 61, 28 Jan. 59, 1958 Undated, 14 Feb. 1957, and 18 June 56. The significance of the figures on "part Acquisitions" is unclear. It includes both the acquisitions of subsidiaries or divisions, which in economic terms are like separate going businesses, the acquisitions of which should be counted in any merger total, and the acquisitions of patents, inventories, or facilities which should not, in general, be included in such a total. Accordingly, the "true" acquisitions lie between the total, and the total less part acquisitions.

[11] The comparison of the recent level with that of 1929 is based on the data in the FTC release of 8 Feb. 63, p. 5. The comparison of the 1929 peak with that of the first great merger movement relies on R. Nelson, *Merger Movements in American Industry* (Princeton: Princeton University Press, 1959), Appendix Table C–7.

type of merger, and size of both acquired and acquiring firms. No such detailed breakdown of the total figures, either on an annual basis or for the whole period, is available. However, we have certain partial measures, covering various samples of firms and varying periods, which provide a useful addition of significant detail.

TABLE 10–1

SELECTED STATISTICS ON MERGERS AND ACQUISITIONS, 1951–63

Year	FTC Total number of acquisitions (1)	Total less part acquisitions (2)	Of which mining and manufacturing (3)	Moody's and SCR Total, mining and manufacturing (4)
1951	703	N.A.	N.A.	235
1952	822	"	"	288
1953	793	"	"	295
1954	617	"	"	387
1955	846	819	689	525
1956	905	837	638	537
1957	941	770	598	490
1958	899	718	543	457
1959	1050	905	719	656
1960	1012	889	700	635
1961	1234	1101	759	671
1962	1261	1095	724	672
1963	1311	1198	1018	N.A.
Total 51–63	12393			5848*
Annual average	952			488*
Total 55–63	9358	8332	6388	4118†
Annual average	1040	926	790	580†

*1951–62
†1955–62

With respect to the size distribution of merging firms, we have a number of breakdowns. First, there is a count of the disappearances through acquisition of mining and manufacturing corporations with assets of $10 million and over in the period 1951–63.[12] There was a total of 585 such, over the period there was a rising trend in the

---

[12] These figures are drawn from the testimony of Dr. Willard F. Mueller, Director of the Bureau of Economics, FTC, before the Subcommittee on Antitrust and Monopoly, Judiciary Committee, Senate on 2 July 1964. I am indebted to Dr. Mueller for making available to us a copy of his testimony, as well as a copy of his paper on "The Significance of Mergers Among Large Manufacturing Firms" given at the University of Connecticut on 22 April 1964.

number, running from an average of about 35 per year in the first half of the period to an average of 57 in the last half. These acquired firms had total assets of $19.3 billion, counting each as of the time of acquisition. The total number of such acquisitions should be compared with the 2447 mining and manufacturing firms in this size class in 1962, and 1892 in 1951. The total assets involved are about 20 percent of the total assets of mining and manufacturing firms in this size class in 1951, and about 10 percent of the corresponding 1962 total.[13]

Next is a count of disappearance by merger in the period 1951–63 of the 1000 largest manufacturing corporations in 1950. Two-hundred-sixteen of these companies—more than one fifth—were absorbed by merger during this time: 163 by other corporations in the group, 37 by manufacturing companies originally smaller, and 16 by non-manufacturing companies. Table 10–2 below shows the distribu-

TABLE 10–2

| 1950 Rank | Acquired Company | | | |
Acquiring Company	Total	1–200	201–500	501–1000
1–200	82	8	35	39
201–500	52	4	12	36
501–1,000	29	1	6	22
Total	163	13	53	97

tion by size of acquired and acquiring companies of the 163 firms which were absorbed within the original group.

Third is a count of the acquisitions made by the 500 largest manufacturing and mining firms over the period 1951–61.[14] In total, these 500 firms made 3400 acquisitions, compared with the total for the same period of nearly 5300 shown by the Moody's and SCR count. (Note that the FTC mining and manufacturing count might run about 30 percent higher.) These acquisitions were distributed among the deciles of the acquiring group as follows:

---

[13] See Statistics of Income for 1951, 1962.

[14] Mergers and Superconcentration, op. cit., Table 16, and Ch. 6. Firms appear to be ranked by 1960 sales. The size boundaries of the deciles were (in $ millions, 1960 sales): 771, 438, 301, 231, 181, 138, 114, 93, 83, 72.

1st	decile	471	6th	decile	257
2nd	"	413	7th	"	250
3rd	"	746	8th	"	203
4th	"	313	9th	"	237
5th	"	320	10th	"	194

The distribution of acquiring firms by the number of acquisitions was:

Number of Acquisitions	Number of Acquiring Firms
0	60
1–5	227
6–10	137
10 or more	66

Among the 50 largest firms only one made no acquisitions during the period; among the second 50, 2; the third, 4; and the fourth, 7.

Finally, more complete information, including some measures of assets as well as frequency counts, is available with respect to the acquisitions of the 200 largest manufacturing corporations from 1951 through 1963.[15] Over the whole period, these companies made almost 2000 acquisitions including part acquisitions. The total assets acquired in the 1056 acquisitions for which information is available was just a little over $15 billion, distributed in terms of size of acquired company as shown in Table 10–3.

TABLE 10–3

ACQUISITIONS OF 200 LARGEST MANUFACTURING
CORPORATIONS OF 1962, 1951–63

Assets Acquired ($ millions)	Number of Acquisitions	Share of Total Assets Acquired, %
Less than 1..........................	308	1
1 to 10...............................	433	12
10 to 50..............................	268	38
50 and over..........................	71	49

The importance of acquisitions as a source of growth for the same group of corporations is shown by size classes in Table 10–4 for the period 1951–62.

---

[15] Mueller, *Testimony*, pp. 37–45, Tables 9–12. These figures refer to the 200 largest corporations in 1962, ranked by assets.

TABLE 10–4

RELATIVE IMPORTANCE OF ACQUISITIONS OF 200 LARGEST MANUFACTURING
CORPORATIONS, 1951–62

Size Rank	Average Assets ($ millions) 1950	1962	Number of Acquisitions Total	Average per firm	Average Value Assets Acquired ($ millions)	Acquired Assets as Percent of 1950 Assets	1962 Assets	Asset Growth
1–5............	2665	7289	30	6	130	4.9	1.8	2.8
6–10...........	1481	3581	35	7	156	10.6	4.4	7.5
11–20..........	824	1947	47	5	28	3.4	1.4	2.5
21–50..........	413	1053	232	8	97	23.5	9.2	15.1
51–100.........	238	612	709	14	98	41.0	16.0	26.1
101–150........	137	353	434	9	44	32.5	12.6	20.5
151–200........	86	281	382	8	41	47.7	17.7	28.0
Total	322	827	1869	9	69	21.6	8.4	13.7

A frequency distribution of the 200 companies by the ratio of growth through acquisition to total asset growth over the same period shows the following:

Percentage Growth by Acquisition	Number of Companies
0 (no Acquisitions).............	16
less than 10%......................	84
(including no asset information)	
10–30...........................	48
30–50...........................	29
50 and over.....................	23

In oversimple summary: mergers among the large firms have been important; a significant number of the large, but not the very largest, manufacturing and mining corporations have disappeared by merger in the period since 1952; almost all of the largest firms in these categories show some merger activity during the period; acquisitions have been a substantial source of assets growth for the large, but not for the very largest, corporations in these groups.

There is much less information on the distribution of mergers by type—horizontal, vertical, conglomerate—than by size. Indeed, we have only two fragmentary items that bear on this question. The first is a tabulation by the FTC covering 2100 mergers occurring between

Jan. 1951 and July 1954.[16] The 2100 mergers were listed as providing the following "advantages" to the acquiring firms:

1. Increased capacity to supply existing markets.......804
2. Lengthened product line.........................479
3. Diversification................................448
4. Backward integration..........................252
5. Market extensions.............................210
6. Forward integration...........................168
7. Other...161

The sum of these is 2540, indicating some mergers had more than one characteristic. If we ignore the category of "other" and redistribute the others to the three categories defined above in percentage terms, based on the total including duplications we get:

Horizontal	(1 and 5)	43
Conglomerate	(2 and 3)	40
Vertical	(4 and 6)	17.

The report on *Mergers and Superconcentration* cited above provides a listing of all the known acquisitions of the 500 largest industrial corporations, 1951–61. Examination of the firms acquired by the 100 largest permitted classification of these acquisitions in terms of the same categories.[17] The 100 largest companies made 761 acquisitions in this period. Sales figures were available covering 266 of these acquisitions. Table 10–5 shows the distribution of numbers of acquired firms and their sales among the three categories. Acquisitions involving close substitutes or geographic market extensions were classified as horizontal.

While these figures are broadly consistent with those covering the first part of the period, they differ considerably in detail, especially in the much greater importance of horizontal mergers in the second sample. Also striking is the much smaller average size of horizontal mergers than of conglomerate and vertical ones, in those cases for which sales information is available.

---

[16] Federal Trade Commission, *Report on Corporate Mergers and Acquisitions* (May, 1955), pp. 49–55. This discussion covers 2091 acquisitions which compares with totals of 2913 mergers recorded by the FTC for the period 1951–54.

[17] *Mergers and Superconcentration, op. cit.,* Table 18. I am indebted to Mr. Donald Skolnick, who made the tabulation. His analysis was made on the basis of information in *Moody's* and the annual reports of the acquiring and acquired corporations. Where the data permitted, sales were split between the various categories involved in a single acquisition. The inconsistency of the count of 761 acquisitions with that used above for the same companies (883) reflects the inclusion in the original list of mergers which could not be traced in the available material.

When we turn from this incomplete description of the character of the merger movement of recent years to a picture of the number and nature of proceedings directed at preventing or undoing mergers, our information is only slightly better.

From 1951 to the end of 1963, the Department of Justice had issued 72 complaints in Section 7 cases, involving some 125 mergers; at the same time the Federal Trade Commission had initiated action in 51 cases, involving some 455 mergers. The rate of enforcement appears to be on the increase, with a greater number of cases initiated in more recent years than in earlier ones, especially by the

TABLE 10–5

ACQUISITIONS OF 100 LARGEST INDUSTRIAL CORPORATIONS 1951–61, BY CATEGORY

	Total	Horizontal	Conglomerate	Vertical
Total number..............	761	532	149	90
Number with sales...........	266	161	70	32
Sales ($ millions)............11686		4914	4799	1973
Average sales ($ million)......	4.4	3.1	6.9	6.2

Anti-Trust Division. Thus actions had been initiated in somewhat fewer than 5 percent of the mergers and acquisitions the FTC had recorded during the period from the passage of the Celler-Kefauver amendment to the end of 1963 and perhaps twice that share of the large mergers. This means that the effect of the relatively few proceedings the enforcement agencies institute in inhibiting mergers which might otherwise take place is also less than it might become when more cases have been tried and legal rules are better developed.

An analysis made for the National Industrial Conference Board by Betty Bock of the 96 cases in which action had been initiated by the end of 1961 illuminates the influence of size and category of merger on the choice of the enforcing agency.[18] Size of both acquiring and acquired company had a positive correlation with action. Three-quarters of the acquiring companies subject to complaints were among the 500 largest manufacturing concerns; more than half among the 200 largest. The acquired companies tended to have

---

[18] Betty Bock, *Mergers and Markets*, National Industrial Conference Board Study in Industrial Economics, #72 (1962). Miss Bock also made an earlier study of the same kind in 1960, with the same title, #69 in the NICB series.

relatively high ranks in the markets in which they sold. Classification
of number of acquisitions by category shows:

Horizontal	86%	
of which horizontal only		61
in combination with vertical		25
Conglomerate and vertical	14	
of which vertical only		10
conglomerate only		2
both		2

Thus the typical complaint in these 96 cases was directed against a
large, high ranking firm acquiring another fairly high ranking firm
selling in the same or a very closely related market. The only purely
conglomerate mergers included in this tabulation were the acquisition of Euclid Road Machinery by General Motors, and that of
Clorox by Procter and Gamble, both of which are discussed below.

In summary then, neither the level of enforcement in total, nor the
level of proceedings against conglomerate mergers suggests that the
policy of the law is, at least as yet, bearing down with a heavy weight
on conglomerate mergers in particular and non-horizontal ones in
general.

SOME RECENT CASES

The most important thing we can say about litigation under
Section 7 as amended, is that Supreme Court decisions have been
few in number, and the majority of these few have dealt with cases in
which simple horizontal elements dominate the factual situation.[19]
Thus any conclusions we draw as to rules of law in more complex
circumstances will be largely speculative and necessarily tentative,
and we will perforce look at lower court and FTC decisions, as well
as complaints in cases not yet decided by any tribunal, rather than

---

[19] So far the Supreme Court has dealt substantively with 9 merger cases under the
1951 Amendment to Section 7, of which 5 were primarily horizontal mergers, one was
vertical, one contained horizontal and vertical elements, and two were conglomerate.
The citations in order are: *U.S. v Virginia and Maryland Milk Producers* 362 US 458
(1960); *U.S. v Bliss and Laughlin* 371 US 70 (1962); *Crown Zellerbach v U.S.* 370
US 937 (1962); *U.S. v Philadelphia National Bank* 374 US 321 (1963); *U.S. v Penn-
Olin Chemical Co.* 84 S. Ct. 1719 (1964); *U.S. v Jerrold Electronics* 365 US 567
(1961); *Brown Shoe v U.S.* 370 US 294 (1961); *U.S. v Alcoa* 84 S. Ct. 1283 (1964);
and *U.S. v Continental Can* 84 S. Ct. 1738 (1964).

attempting to construe only the few authoritative decisions of the Court.

The Supreme Court has so far dealt with substantive issues in three cases of conglomerate mergers: Continental Can-Hazel Atlas, Alcoa-Rome Cable and Penn-Olin Chemical Co. In all three cases, the District Courts found against the government; the Supreme Court reversed all three decisions, rendering a final decision on legality in the first two cases, and directing the District Court to pursue further the question of competitive effects in the third.[20]

In 1955, Continental Can, the slightly smaller of the two can manufacturers who between them still dominate the industry (71 percent of all metal container shipments, and a higher proportion of general-line packers cans) acquired Hazel-Atlas, third largest producer in the glass bottle industry. This was a substantially less-concentrated industry, with the three largest firms accounting for about 55 percent of the market; Hazel-Atlas' own share was just short of 10 percent. The District Court, in finding for the defendants, argued that the merger was a conglomerate one, and that the Government had failed to make any showing that it would affect competition in either the can market or the various separate markets for glass jars. Further, the Court found that the Government had failed to establish a persuasive definition of any market (line of commerce) in which competitive effects could be observed. Of all those that the Government offered, only the market for beer containers was a well defined market in which cans and bottles were in competition; however, Hazel-Atlas' production of beer bottles was so small as to give no basis for attributing to the merger an effect on competition in that market. The Court (two justices dissenting) relied on two points: a different construction of what were relevant markets, and a different assessment of the significance of the elimination of potential competition. Citing direct competition between bottles and glass in soft drinks, baby foods, and broader competition in packaging toiletries, cosmetics, medicines and household products, the Court defines a broad market in the combined metal and glass container industry, in which Continental, the second ranking firm supplied 22 percent of the output, Hazel-Atlas, the fifth ranking, 3 percent, and the five largest firms in aggregate about 70 percent.

---

[20] The District Court citations in the three cases are: *U.S.* v. *Penn Olin* 217 F. Supp. 110; *U.S.* v *Alcoa* 214 F. Supp. 501; and *U.S.* v *Continental Can* 217 F. Supp. 761.

Even without consideration of potential competition, the merger of two firms in this market context would be clearly illegal in terms of Brown Shoe and Philadelphia National Bank. The importance of potential competitive developments in the rivalry of bottle and cans, and the possibility that the instant merger would, if sanctioned, lead to other similar ones, which together would sharply reduce or eliminate this competitive potential was the second ground of the Court's decision.

Aluminum Company of America's acquisition of Rome Cable Company presents similar features, both in the underlying facts and the way they were treated by the Courts. Alcoa, the largest integrated producer of primary aluminum and fabricated products, including aluminum wire and cable, acquired Rome in 1959. Rome was a producer of wire and cable, primarily insulated wire and cable, about 90 percent of which was of copper. For a few years prior to the acquisition, Rome had produced a few of the simpler varieties of insulated aluminum wire for Alcoa on a toll basis. At the time Alcoa had no facilities or technical knowledge in the insulating field; its own production having been limited to bare aluminum wire and cable. The District Court, finding that the bare aluminum wire and cable (including steel-core aluminum cable) which were Alcoa's chief products and the insulated wire and cable of various types (of both copper and aluminum) which were Rome's chief products were sold in separate markets, characterized the merger as chiefly a conglomerate one. The horizontal element of the merger was small, and further, Alcoa's market share in the products which both Alcoa and Rome sold actually declined after the merger. The elimination of potential competition arising from the possibility that Alcoa would have independently entered the insulated field and Rome the bare aluminum field could not be construed as a substantial lessening of competition. The Supreme Court, in overruling the judgment below (three justices dissenting), again found a market definition—aluminum conductor, bare and insulated, which the District Court had rejected as a market definition supported by the evidence—within which the merger was essentially horizontal. Alcoa was the dominant producer in this market with nearly 28 percent of the output; the largest three producers accounted for more than three-quarters of the market. In this context, the addition of Rome's 1.3 percent share by merger was a violation of the statute.

The third of these cases presents a somewhat different set of issues, since it involves a joint-venture with horizontal and vertical as well as conglomerate elements. Penn-Olin Chemical is a joint venture, owned 50 percent each by Pennsalt Chemicals Corp. and Olin-Mathieson Chemicals Corp., with its officers and directors drawn in equal numbers from the officers of the two. In 1961, Penn-Olin constructed a sodium perchlorate plant in Calvert, Kentucky, with capacity of some 26 thousand tons per year. Pennsalt was to operate the plant; Olin, to market its output. Previous to this, Pennsalt had produced sodium chlorate in Portland, Oregon; the major producers in the Southeast were American Potash at Aberdeen, Mississippi, which also had a plant in Henderson, Nevada, and Hooker Chemical at Columbus, Mississippi, which had another plant at Niagara Falls. When the joint venture was formed, consumption in the Southeast, mostly by pulp and paper mills, was 57 percent of the U.S. total; another 22 percent was consumed West of the Rockies. Olin was not a producer at all. For a brief period it had acted as marketing agent for Pennsalt in the Southeast, since it sold other chemicals to the pulp and paper producers. Olin was a producer of sodium chlorate in Niagara Falls, for which sodium chlorate purchased from Hooker was an input. Olin and Pennsalt were major competitors in another chemical, sodium hypochlorite, in which they jointly accounted for between 75 percent and 90 percent of the market. In finding for the defendant, the District Court dealt with the Southeast as a separate market. Thus the joint venture did not restrict competition between Pennsalt operating in Portland, and the new producer in Kentucky. The new producer increased rather than diminished competition in the Southeast; and the later entry of Pittsburgh Plate Glass with another new plant in Louisiana showed further the lack of adverse effect of the joint venture. Had Penn-Olin not been created, the evidence supports the inference that one of Pennsalt or Olin-Mathieson would have entered the Southeastern market, but not the inference that both of them would. Accordingly, the mere substitution of Penn-Olin for whichever firm would have entered in its absence cannot be considered as substantially lessening competition. Further, the joint venture in sodium chlorate in Kentucky could not in itself provide the basis for an inference that there would be an impact on competition between the two firms in other chemicals, such as sodium hypochlorite, nor for an inference that the market represented by Olin's purchases of sodium chlorate for its Niagara plant, heretofore supplied by Hooker, would be foreclosed from competition and reserved to Penn-Olin. A majority of the Supreme Court reversed the District Court, holding that the joint venture did foreclose potential competition. Even if only one of the two partners would have entered the Southeastern market, the other would have retained the possibility of so doing at a later date, and this entry potential might have affected the nature of actual competition in the market. The case was remanded for further findings on whether the foreclosure of potential competition did in fact have substantial effects. One dissenter (or two) agreed with the court below; two felt that the facts justified the conclusion that elimination of the competitive potential of one of the joint venturers, in the context of the rapidly growing market, already had an illegal anti-competitive effect, and thus no further proceedings were necessary. The conglomerate aspects of the merger played no role in the Court's argument, but the weight given to potential competition is clearly important in speculating on the future development of law on conglomerate mergers.

Five cases not dealt with by the Supreme Court deserve some examination. The first is the acquisition of Clorox by Procter and Gamble, which the FTC has held illegal and ordered divested; a decision now under appeal. The second is the case against Ingersoll-Rand's proposed acquisitions of several machinery manufacturers, which was settled by a consent decree, after the trial court granted an interlocutory decree against the acquisitions. The third and fourth are still pending in the courts of first instance: complaints against General Motors' acquisition of Euclid Road Machinery and Chrysler's proposed acquisition of Mack Truck. The fifth, a decision by the Court of Appeals upholding the Federal Trade Commission finding that the acquisition by Reynolds Metal of Arrow Brands, a converter of aluminum foil, was illegal, has not been appealed further, and so is final.[21]

Procter and Gamble is one of the nations' largest firms and one of the three largest sellers of soaps, detergents and cleansers. Lever

[21] The Commission decision in Procter and Gamble, docket number 6901, was in November 1963. The Ingersoll-Rand consent decision was entered by District Court (W. D., Pa.) on 3 April 64; the Appeals Court's opinion upholding the interlocutory decree was 320 F2d 509. The complaints against GM and Chrysler were filed, respectively, in 1959 and 1964. The Reynolds Metal decision was 309 F2d 223.

Brothers and Colgate-Palmolive are the other similar large sellers in this area; together they account for some 80 percent of total sales of these products, and P and G alone accounts for nearly 55 percent. Clorox, with sales of about $40 million at the time of the acquisition, was the largest manufacturer of household liquid bleach, supplying nearly half the market. Bleach was its only output; in terms of sales it was about one-twenty-fifth the size of P and G. Neither P and G nor its major rivals sold household liquid bleach. However, Purex, the second firm in that field, with about one-sixth the market, also manufactured detergents, soaps and cleansers, and was the fourth largest seller in the field, but with less than 5 percent of the total market. Clorox maintained its competitive superiority by advertising, since there are apparently no significant economies of scale in production or differences between one liquid bleach and another. In ruling the acquisition illegal, the FTC relied chiefly on the argument that the superior advertising and marketing capabilities of P and G—whose total annual expenditures on advertising of all types reached nearly $100 million, with another $50 million for other sales promotion efforts—would enable it to increase Clorox' already dominant position and entrench it further. The structure of advertising discount rates contributed greatly to the probability of this result. Entry of new competitors with branded products, already difficult, would become impossible. The FTC described the merger as a product extension merger rather than a true conglomerate, in the sense that the bleach and P and G's own products are complementary in use, and share the same marketing channels, rather than being entirely unrelated. Some weight is put on P and G's ability to use the leverage provided by its dominant position in other products to promote shelving and displaying of Clorox bleach in supermarkets, which are the most important channels of sale.

Ingersoll-Rand, a large manufacturer of compressors, pumps, rock drilling equipment, hoists, and other similar industrial machinery, agreed to acquire three firms producing various kinds of coal-mining machinery, which Ingersoll-Rand had not previously made. These three firms constituted half the number of suppliers of their lines of machinery in the U.S. Their combined shares of various specific types of machines ranged from 30 percent to 60 percent of the market totals, and had been increasing in recent years. Total sales of these types of machinery amounted to some $80 million per year;

somewhat less than half of Ingersoll-Rand's total sales. The Court of Appeals, sustaining an interlocutory decree to bar the acquisitions pending the outcome of the suit, found that if carried through, they posed a substantial threat of making Ingersoll-Rand the dominant supplier and only full-line supplier of coal mining machinery. Ingersoll-Rand ultimately entered into a consent settlement under which it consummated the transaction with one of the three companies, and agreed to acquire no other firms in the industry for ten years without the approval of the Court. Here again, conglomerate and horizontal elements were both present.

The two complaints bearing on acquisitions of non-automobile producers by General Motors and Chrysler, respectively, also involve conglomerate mergers. General Motors, the largest U.S. industrial corporation and the dominant producer in the concentrated automobile market, acquired Euclid, the largest producer of off-the-road trucks, used in construction, with about 50 percent of that market. Euclid's sales, prior to acquisition, were about $33 million; General Motors' about three-hundred times as large. The complaint alleged that competition in the off-the-road truck market would be damaged, because Euclid's already leading position would be reinforced, and other competitors could not stand up against the overall power of GM. Further, GM had a vertical relation to the market, since it was a supplier of diesel engines, transmissions, and other parts. The merger therefore would involve foreclosure of a substantial part of this trade to GM's competitors. Finally, GM itself was a potential competitor of Euclid, and the merger eliminated potential competition.

Chrysler, the third largest automobile producer and the twelfth largest industrial firm in the U.S., proposed to acquire Mack Truck, one of the two largest independent manufacturers of heavy trucks. Mack supplied its own diesel engines, and was increasing its capacity to produce them; Chrysler was a purchaser of diesel engines for use in its medium duty trucks. The complaint alleged that the merger would eliminate potential competition between Chrysler and Mack, as well as involving foreclosure in respect to the market for diesel engines represented by Chrysler.

Finally, the acquisition of Arrow Brands by Reynolds Metals is worth noting, even though it was strictly a vertical merger. Reynolds is the largest manufacturer of aluminum foil; Arrow was a small converter, buying aluminum foil and processing it for special use by florists. The Court of Appeals, in upholding the FTC finding that the merger was illegal, relied on the argument that Reynolds' superior financial resources, applied to the small decorative foil converting market, would enable Arrow to dominate its rivals by cutting prices to or below costs. This proposition, combined with the fact of price reductions and the growth of Arrow's market share, was the basis for the finding. Conceivably, the use of such an argument could outlaw the acquisition of any company in a small unit industry by any relatively large firm, and thus place very severe restrictions on conglomerate mergers.

What do these cases, decisions and complaints taken all together, show about the direction in which the law is being applied to conglomerate mergers? At first glance, they seem to go quite far in the direction of flat prohibition, but a more cautious appraisal suggests a different result. First, the arguments of *Reynolds Metal* must be rejected as bad law as well as bad economics. The "rich parent" or "deep pocket" theory as baldly stated in that case goes far beyond the bounds of likely effects on market competition to speculation about the possibilities of what would be illegal or predatory conduct on the part of the acquiring firm in Robinson-Patman or Section 5 terms—as well as irrational conduct in economic terms, unless further facts are shown which explain why cutting prices to or below costs made sense. The theory certainly has not been used in those cases the Supreme Court has decided and it seems unlikely that it will be adopted by the majority of the Court in any further case.

Next, the result in *Ingersoll-Rand*, interpreted in the light of the decree, appeared to turn on the horizontal effect of the elimination of competition among the three firms which Ingersoll-Rand proposed to acquire. Together, they accounted for large, and in some cases majority, shares in the relatively small and concentrated markets in the various types of coal-mining machinery. Since the decree allowed the acquisition of one of the firms—provided it was the only one—it was not conglomerate integration as such that was the focus of the action.

In both Continental Can and Alcoa, the arguments used by the majority in reversing the courts below rested on broadening or narrowing, respectively, market boundaries so as to redefine each situation as one of horizontal merger. In neither case do the facts—as recited in each pair of opinions—support the market definition the Court has adopted; in this respect, the lower court decisions appear nearer the mark in both. The FTC opinion in P and G does not depend on finding a definition of the market which makes the case one of horizontal merger. There is a clear cut statement that the market in which the merger will affect competition adversely is the market for household bleach. Yet there is also emphasis on the proposition that the merger was a "product extension" merger rather than a true conglomerate, and recital of the extent to which there were complementarities in advertising, sales promotion, and distribution between bleach and the rest of the P and G line. But the major ground for decision is that the merger will transform conditions of competition in the bleach market in an undesirable way. This of course goes more squarely to the central issue of how the competitive effects of a conglomerate merger can and should be evaluated.

There is at least one way in which the results in these three cases can be rationalized in terms which are consistent not only for them, but for Penn-Olin and the complaints against GM and Chrysler as well, and which does not depend on an essentially arbitrary definition of market boundaries which allows a tribunal to assimilate any merger to the rule of the Philadelphia National Bank case.[22] Mergers other than simply horizontal are forbidden when : (1) the acquiring firm is very large in absolute size and the dominant firm, or one of the few dominant firms in a concentrated market; (2) the acquired firm operates in a market which is itself fairly concentrated, and in which entry barriers are already significant; and (3) the merger threatens to raise entry barriers still further, by presenting would-be rivals with significantly poorer prospects of success than existed in the market before the entrance by merger of the large firm; or (4) the acquiring firm and others in its industry represent the most important potential competitors for the firms in the industry of the acquired, perhaps because there is similarity of technology (GM-Euclid, Chrysler-Mack) or close competition or complementarity in use, and similarity of marketing channels (Alcoa-Rome, P and G-Clorox, Continental-Hazel Atlas) or both (Penn-Olin).

This rule can be given a perfectly sensible economic rationale, consistent with the reasons why we do and should value competition,

---

[22] Bock, *op. cit.*

and not dependent simply on a preference for preserving the existing market positions of small firms. In essence, that rationale turns on the general preference, other things being equal, for larger numbers and lower entry barriers over smaller numbers and higher entry barriers in any market, on the view that the preferred conditions are in general more conducive to effective competition. Thus a change in structure, in a market in which there is already some significant element of concentration, in the direction of raising entry barriers, and/or eliminating the possibility that particular potential competitors will come in as additional suppliers, rather than entering via the absorption of existing sellers, is *prima facie,* undesirable.

The qualifiers, however, are necessary, because changing technologies of production and marketing may promise substantial cost-savings through changes in scale which reduce numbers and raise entry barriers. In general, the main line of antitrust policy has been to refrain from interfering with concentrated market structures that appear to be determined by efficiency considerations, and the writer, along with most economists, considers this the appropriate policy.[23] Judgments about efficiency are notoriously difficult, however, and nowhere more so than in respect to the economies of unified ownership of several different technical units operating in different, though related markets.[24] There is every reason to avoid—if at all possible—giving courts the task of determining which of the mergers falling in our general description, are and which are not justified on efficiency grounds, since this is a task to which the trial process is singularly ill-suited.

But there appears to be a path between the unconditional condemnation of all conglomerate mergers because they may have the possibility of producing the kind of effects described, and the necessity of turning each such proceeding into the kind of inquiry—if there be such—which would support a confident judgment as to whether there were cost savings available or probable which would justify the merger. This is to let the presumption be against the merger in the situation where the acquiring firm is a giant, and already one of the leaders in one or more large concentrated markets. Put otherwise, the presumption should be against the

---

[23] C. Kaysen and D. F. Turner, *op. cit.,* pp. 45, 100–119.

[24] See D. Bok, "Section 7 of the Clayton Act and the Merging of Law and Economics," *Harvard Law Review,* Dec. 1960.

very largest firms expanding by merger in almost every case, unless the absence of effect on competition is clear. Under such a rule, it is worth noting, the facts in Reynolds Metal seem to support a judgment that there would have been no significant competitive effect, and the merger should have been allowed. The foil converting market appeared to be one in which entry would be relatively easy, no matter what Reynolds' policies were, unless it engaged in price discrimination in an irrational as well as an illegal manner.

Thus interpreted, the proposed rule should not create substantially more difficult problems of proof and argument than are now inherent in Section 7 cases. In particular, the existence of economies of scale and integration would not be available as a defence to the large acquirer in cases fulfilling the conditions of probable competitive effect set forth above.

CONCLUSIONS

Prohibiting the largest firms from expanding by merger in such circumstances would not amount in any sense to an absolute bar to conglomerate integration by merger, or a denial to all firms, and therefore to the economy, of gains in efficiency and adaptations to changing market circumstances which such mergers might provide. It would still be open for smaller sellers to make such acquisitions, as it would be open to the large ones to achieve the gains of integration—if they justify the effort—by entry into the new market on the basis of constructing a new plant. Thus in the Alcoa-Rome case, what was forbidden to Alcoa need not have been forbidden to Harvey of Ormat; or alternatively, if the insulated wire and cable market looked attractive, Alcoa could have hired the engineers and salesmen and invested in the plant necessary to enter the market.

What we have described may or may not be the policy in the minds of enforcement agencies and judges; there is as yet too little evidence on which to judge. Assuming, for argument, that it should be, it still raises at least three problems. First is the usual question of where to draw the line. How big does a firm have to be absolutely and relatively to its market in order to fall within the ban? Here no formula is possible, except to say that the discretion of the enforcement agencies supplies an element that is indispensable, and that the Courts cannot supply.

The second question is whether a rule which forbids conglomerate growth by merger to some companies while permitting it to their competitors is "fair" or "reasonable." This, in turn, must be answered in terms of whether there is a policy interest served by such discrimination which justifies it. The history of growth by mergers in the past, and the presence of substantial non-competitive elements outside the reach of antitrust policy as presently conceived in the markets in which many of the largest firms operate appear to this writer a sufficient justification for what may be viewed as an extra obstacle to their future growth by merger. This is certainly an innocuous form for the Congressional preference for the small business—of which the Celler-Kefauver amendment was certainly an expression, however we read the statutory language—to take, as compared with other possibilities.

Finally, it is clear that the operation of this rule will do something to narrow the market for going businesses and business assets. The sellers in that market, the smaller firms which are generally the acquired firms in the merger transactions we have been considering, will pay the price for such a change. In general, the largest firms, which the proposed rule would remove from the market, would be in the position to offer the best terms to the owners of firms they acquire. Indeed, to the extent that the presumption that some prospects of market domination entered into the calculations of the acquiring firm is correct, the price it could rationally offer would be higher than that of a buyer without such prospects. It is difficult, or impossible, to estimate the magnitude of this effect, but it must be accepted as part of the price of pro-competitive policy, not all the burdens of which fall on large firms with large market shares. It is perhaps an acceptable irony that Congressional zeal for protecting small business should be expressed in ways that are not without perverse effects. But irony aside, it is clear that the maintenance of a market for going businesses is an important aspect of resource mobility, and freedom of entry and exit. A too harsh application of Section 7, which in effect forbade mergers at all past some absolute size levels would certainly be undesirable in this as in other contexts. But though we lack quantitative information to guide us, it seems a safe speculation that the present enforcement policy in terms of both rules and level of effort is still far from the danger point in this respect.

The kind of policy toward conglomerate merger would be consistent with allowing mergers to play a positive role in the kind of adaptation to change in markets and technology on which the proponents of the "new competition" have put so much emphasis. It would however, place a heavier weight on the old reliable elements of the old competition, number and entry barriers, than at least some exponents of the "new" think necessary. Presently, it is too soon to judge whether or not a standard which approximates this is being put into practice. The available evidence from the decisions is not inconsistent with such a standard, though the opinions of the Supreme Court can hardly be said to articulate it. Further, a perusal of the list of conglomerate mergers which have not as yet been the subject of enforcement proceedings suggests that, if anything, the enforcement agencies are using a more, rather than less, generous standard than the one suggested. Such mergers as Ford's acquisition of Philco, Martin's acquisition of American Marietta, Coca-Cola's of Minute-Maid, Goodyear's of Rayco and International Harvester's of Solar Aircraft may not on close examination all fill the criteria suggested above, but it appears likely that some of them do.[25] But in the matter of enforcement criteria, as in the matter of rules of decision by the Court, it may be necessary to wait. The whole of our arguments suggests, however, that from an economist's viewpoint we can wait, since we are not under the necessity of reversing a current which has already run too far too fast.

---

[25] *Mergers and Superconcentration, op. cit.*, Table 18.

In this essay on competition, Heflebower is concerned partly with innovation, but more broadly with all factors affecting the relevance of orthodox price theory today. He weighs the "received" theory of competition and finds it wanting, stating that its formal elegance is not matched with comparable utility when applied to the real world. Various improvements are suggested in an attempt to develop a more complete explanation of different market organizations, practices, and performance.

RICHARD B. HEFLEBOWER is Professor of Economics at Northwestern University. He attended Fresno State College for his A.B. degree and the University of California where he received his Ph.D. degree. His publications include *Full Costs, Cost Changes and Prices in Business, Concentration and Public Policy,* "Toward a Theory of Industrial Markets and Prices," *AER Proceedings,* 1954, and "Mass Distribution: A Phase of Bilateral Oligopoly or of Competition?" *AER Proceedings,* 1957.

CHAPTER 11

COMPETITION: STATIC,
DYNAMIC, DATED

R. B. Heflebower*

The original general topic for these forum sessions, "Modern Competitive Theory," suggests that the existing theory has not enabled us to explain the observed performance of industrial markets. Alternatively, modern could connote that the structure of the problem, namely, how markets made up of private enterprises perform, has changed significantly from, say, the pre-war era. The reasons might be that important influences affecting sellers, such as the objectives of the management-controlled large corporations, the length of life of capital goods, and the rate of changes of production functions, provide a significantly different decision-making environment than that assumed implicitly in price theory. All of these interpretations of the conference theme are challenges to the universality in time and place of orthodox price theory as "descriptive" or "positive economics." An evaluation of such implications and a consideration of improvements in the theory of market organization and performance are the tasks of this paper.

PRICE THEORY AND ITS METHODOLOGY

In the present context, "old" must refer to the price theory developed in the 'thirties under such labels as monopolistic or imperfect competition.[1] This includes the extension of duopoly theory to the

---

* The author acknowledges the helpful comments of his colleague, Jerome Rothenberg.
[1] It will be seen below (under the section heading "Marshall-like But Not Fully So") that the monopolistic-imperfect competition theory has not been accepted everywhere as the received doctrine.

larger-number oligopoly cases and the formal development of the theory of differentiation.[2] By this concept Chamberlin split up the commodity of Marshall into narrow differentiated "products" or "items," typically each produced by a separate firm. Price theory became the "theory of the firm" to this school but of a firm surrounded by substitutes that ranged in closeness (cross-elasticities of demand and of supply) from almost perfect to no substitutability. In substance, however, groupings of firms on the bases of closeness of substitution reformulated the broader concept of a market and of an industry, particularly by economists trained in this theory who then engaged in intensive empirical research. A distinction emerged, progressively, between the large numbers of sellers of close substitutes, who presumably act without regard to rivals' counteractions, and the small numbers whose every turn is conditioned by expectations of rivals' responses, the oligopoly cases. For such a product, and for a broader market also, methods of rivalry or agreement, and the economic outcome thereof, were expected to be determined by market structure in the very narrow usage of the number and size distribution of sellers and of buyers. For consumer goods, particularly, the effect of product differentiation on costs and prices was part of the theory. A unique welfare conclusion derived from this theory is that in industries not purely competitive or, alternatively, purely monopolistic, excess capacity characterizes equilibria,[3] a conclusion that has become part of a neo-Marxist criticism of capitalism.[4]

---

[2] Two additional points should be noted. More or less as a by-product of the development of imperfect competition theory there occurred a "perfecting" of the theory of "pure" or "perfect" competition. (For a usage that distinguishes pure and perfect competition, see note 18 below.) Second, whether the equilibria of the monopolistic or imperfect competition theory, including much of the theorizing about oligopoly, are short-run or long-run is not clear. Chamberlin claims his theory is long-run. But this literature does not contain, as does Marshall's, an exposition of the process of adjustment among different lengths of run.

[3] This conclusion is to a substantial degree inaccurate. Harold Demsetz has shown that Chamberlin's tangency solution, i.e., large-number monopolistic competition cases is not a necessary outcome ("The Nature of Equilibrium in Monopolistic Competition," *Journal of Political Economy*, LXVII, February, 1959, pp. 21–30). Roy F. Harrod (*Economic Essays*, New York: Harcourt, Brace and World, 1952, pp. 140–157) points to the error in the assumption that firms would install excess capacity in either large-number or small-number cases.

[4] As by Paul Baran, *The Political Economy of Growth* (Peoples Publishing House, 1957).

Empirical research into the organization and performance of particular markets for manufactured goods has shown that additional and more varied (than size distribution of firms) features of markets are important. So far no complete, definitive, and demonstrably valid theory has emerged from this research. However, this theory and empirical research, with full recognition of its deficiencies, guided the intensive critique of present public policy by Kaysen and Turner.[5] Their theme is that present law is inadequate to deal with "market power created by jointly acting oligopolists."[6]

Beyond being limited to predicting performance by use of at most two variables, monopolistic-imperfect competition theory, like all formal price theory, is "static" and, in substance, also "stationary."[7] It abstracts from problems of limited information, or resource immobility, and of all other influences that, by influencing the adjustment process from one equilibrium position to another, might affect the properties of the new equilibrium. This does not mean that adjustments are thought to be timeless, but that the fact that time is required does not affect the outcome. The properties of an equilibrium and of adjustment are specified as if adjustment were made instantaneously and without limited information or resource immobility having an effect on the equilibrium. While the theory does not ignore change in technology or growth or decline of demand—nonstationary elements—it assumes that these developments are "absorbable" by the system and merely define the new equilibrium position. It is not surprising that such a theoretical framework appears artificial and unduly simple to the uninitiated, but it has been the means of most of the progress in the economics of price and output determination.

Not merely laymen but also some noted economists have protested that market processes are dynamic. This is a popular theme among antitrust lawyers in private practice and underlies a recent vigorous attack on current antitrust law and its enforcement.[8] Schumpeter fed

---

[5] Carl Kaysen and Donald F. Turner, *Antitrust Policy: An Economic and Legal Analysis* (Cambridge: Harvard University Press, 1959).

[6] *Ibid.*, p. 110.

[7] Particularly in that the effect of growing demand on the adjustment process is usually ignored.

[8] Robert H. Bork and Ward S. Bowman, "The Crisis in Antitrust," *Fortune*, December, 1963, pp. 138–40, 192–201.

the fire in his most provocative but unsystematic writing.[9] J. M. Clark had the limits of static analysis in mind when he posed a form of what has come to be called the doctrine of the "second-best":

If there are, for example, five conditions, all of which are essential to perfect competition and the first is lacking in a given case, then it no longer follows that we are necessarily better off for the presence of any one of the other four. In the absence of the first (e.g., perfect two-way mobility of the factors of production) it is *a priori* quite possible that the second and third may become positive detriments; and a workably satisfactory result may depend on achieving some degree of "imperfection" in these other two factors.[10]

The immobility, e.g., of fixed capital, means that investment decisions involve uncertainty and, following a disturbance, this immobility may affect the new equilibrium as well as the time required for adjustment. If it does the problem is dynamic and the predictions based on static theory may be invalid.[11] But Clark's attempts to deal positively with dynamic problems can hardly be termed successful.[12]

Dynamic is sometimes used as a catch-all synonym for change, but when used precisely, change is dynamic only when time enters in an essential way. Adjustment toward a new equilibrium must be affected significantly by such facts as that those making the decisions (firms and households) do so without accurate knowledge of the future, or that leads and lags in the adjustment process force revisions of decision-makers' plans or, more generally, that they revise their plans as the adjustment proceeds and more information is obtained. The most pervasive and potentially dynamic element is lack of knowledge of the future about possible developments for which experience does not provide the decision-maker with an

---

[9] J. A. Schumpeter, *Capitalism, Socialism, and Democracy* (New York: Harper & Bros., 1942), pp. 81–106.

[10] J. M. Clark, "Toward a Concept of Workable Competition," *American Economic Review*, Vol. XXX, No. 2, Part 1 (June, 1940), p. 243.

[11] But businessmen do make major decisions even when quite uncertain of the future. In the formal price theory of recent years, uncertainty has often been "removed" by assuming a "certainty equivalent" in the form of the subjective estimate of the most probable future value of a variable, weighted by the subjective distribution of possible outcomes. While this procedure closes the gap in static theory formally, it makes testing of the theory difficult if not impossible.

[12] Neither in the later sections of the article just cited, in his "Competition: Static Models and Dynamic Aspects," *American Economic Review*, Vol. XLV (1955), pp. 450–62, nor in his *Competition as a Dynamic Process* (Washington, D.C.: Brookings Institution, 1961).

objective probability distribution of possible outcomes. Hence he is faced with uncertainty in the strict sense. This is not serious where resources are highly mobile, as in some trading operations, for errors can then be corrected quickly. But capital once committed in specialized equipment on one site is quite immobile. Hence decisions may be affected by future time in the sense of "analytical time," not of "calendar time" or of the conditions or events of particular dates and places.

The latter kind of "times" is "historical" or what I refer to here as "dated." It could be that the institutional framework within which competition works is meaningfully different than decades ago. Or it could mean that the values of certain variables are beyond the limits of the data assumed implicitly earlier and that the shapes of the functions are different in their extended ranges of today. It could connote also that dynamic processes through time are far more important now; perhaps resources have become much less mobile or that technological change has become more important than are the properties of equilibria under given technological conditions. A possible historical influence, but one that is not embarrassing to orthodox competitive theory formally, is the enhancement of cross elasticities of demand among products made of different materials or by different processes under modern technology.[13]

COMPETITION: SOURCES, FORMS, DEGREES

If one were to add to the economist's varied usages, those of businessmen, public officials, and lawyers, the widely different ideas as to what constitutes competition would become apparent. To most businessmen it means rivalry with identified firms, to the degree that their expected responses enter significantly into the first firm's decisions. To economists rivalry so conditioned reflects the absence of economically effective competition in direct proportion to such awareness. These differing views involve not only issues about forms but also about degrees of competition that are economically beneficial.

The theory of competition in its full compass involves three

---

[13] These paragraphs summarize the usage of terms as developed in Paul A. Samuelson, *Foundations of Economic Analysis* (Cambridge: Harvard University Press, 1946), pp. 312–17.

interrelated topics: (1) What is competitive behavior in the economic sense? (2) What form(s) and degree of competition, including the promptness with which it develops in the event of a disequilibrium, are most beneficial economically? (3) What gives rise to the form and degree of competition one observes? This is the problem of prediction from a system of explanatory variables, the center of interest here.

To clear the air, I offer a definition of competitive behavior, in the economic sense, that does not pre-judge the effects of any particular form or degree of rivalry. The critical feature of competition and of its extent, is the degree of independence of decision-making on the part of each seller and each buyer with respect to the employment of the relevant means (to be explained in a moment) of enhancing his real income. Obviously independence goes beyond lack of overt collusion to include lack of "conjectural independence" or concern on the part of each seller (and of each buyer) about the reactions of other firms to his rivalrous moves. The relevant method of competition (as used here) is not necessarily the one employed, for the latter might have been selected because it was expected to bring minimal effective counteraction by rivals. The one employed is, therefore, the form which the firm concludes will maximize the value of the enterprise. But the relevant form, in the economic sense, is the one, which, had the firm not been concerned about rivals' reaction and had its choice been rational, would have been expected to maximize the value of the firm.[14] (Note that no assumption has been made that unfettered economic competition as thus defined is always best in the economic sense.)

Competitive behavior can be observed most easily when there has been a substantial change in the level of demand for a more or less continuously produced commodity, while prices of variable inputs are constant. Then in response to a change of demand, the price would slide up or down the horizontally summed marginal cost curves of the sellers. The margin between average variable cost and price would expand or contract according to the direction of change of demand. Volume would move in the same direction and by the

---

[14] This criterion permits one to include as economic competition sales effort that provides valid information to buyers or is an essential ingredient of genuine product in innovation, but not sales effort undertaken because price competition is stopped by conjectural restraints when (in the absence of those restraints) it would not be the most profitable device.

amount warranted by the new level and elasticity of demand and the elasticity of supply.

Lacking empirical information about marginal costs one can learn a great deal about the extent to which a market is competitive, by means of price, by what happens to the gross margin over average variable cost. Under competition it should rise when demand increases and shrink when demand declines. On the other hand, with demand given, movements of prices of variable inputs should have little effect on the gross margin; product prices would move to "pass through" in large part changes in the level of marginal cost.[15] This behavior is of a short calendar period sort, sometimes called "cyclical." But one can assert with confidence that longer-run adjustments will not be thwarted in a market that behaves as just sketched.

The reverse need not be true, however. A market with the characteristics and forms of rivalry that serve substantially to lessen, if not to halt, price-change reaction to temporary disequilibria, may lose its potency progressively with the passage of time. Clearly product supply and demand curves become more elastic when one compares them at the beginning of a disequilibrium period with their properties as the period is longer and longer. The same must hold (but to what degree is less clear) with respect to the imagined revenue curves of firms in markets with a substantial degree of concentration. Indeed, some economists' test of competition is applicable to a longer period.[16] Others specifically find no harm but positive good in commodity price (if pressed they probably would say, gross margin) stability in short calendar periods.[17]

Competitive behavior, as defined here, can mean independence of action with respect to research, to innovation, or to capacity adjustments in response to changes in level of demand or in a firm's own costs. But judging both the degree of independence in use, and benefits of, these forms of rivalry are far more difficult. For example, through some date in the 1920's automobile owners gained more

---

[15] For a full development of this argument, see Alfred C. Neal, *Industrial Competition and Price Inflexibility* (Washington: American Council on Public Affairs, 1942), pp. 23–90.

[16] Kaysen and Turner, *op. cit.*, p. 104, and George J. Stigler, "Perfect Competition, Historically Contemplated," *Journal of Political Economy*, Vol. 65, February, 1957, p. 16. (More will be said about the relevant time period.)

[17] Edward S. Mason, *Economic Concentration and the Monopoly Problem* (Cambridge: Harvard University Press, 1957), p. 176.

from the dramatic-improvement in the quality of tires than could have resulted from more avid price competition for tires of the previous quality. This and many similar examples involve a troublesome question, to be considered later, as to whether a necessary condition for improvement of tires was a substantial minimization of short-time price competition.

TYPES OF CRITICISM OF THE RECEIVED THEORY OF COMPETITION

The criticisms of what has been denoted here as the old theory of competition are put in three categories, but they do not follow a single principle of classification. For this and other reasons there is considerable overlapping among the criticisms.

Perfect Competition: Useful Concept or Bugaboo?

Major confusion among economists, and a barrier to discussion between them and laymen, arises from the concept of "pure" and "perfect competition."[18] Formally, it is a method of stating a "norm" or the criterion of optimal behavior of a single market viewed by itself. By definition, cost, output, and price will be in optimal relationships to each other when a market with the structural properties of "pure" competition and the informational qualities of "perfect" competition is in equilibrium.[19] But stating the norm as a type of market, a purely and perfectly competitive one, is both bad semantics and a barrier to understanding. Actually the optimum can be specified, as it is in other parts of economic literature, without using a term that implies a particular type of market. When one turns to positive or descriptive economics, there is no reason to expect, given the basic conditions that exist in nearly all industries, that a market of the structural features of pure competition will, in fact, perform as well as one that departs significantly from that form, since the other feature, perfect competition, rarely if ever exists.

The most systematic critique of perfect competition (used to

---

[18] "Pure" is used to refer to the structural feature of large numbers of sellers and buyers of a standardized product, and "perfect" to indicate the full information (or alternatively, full mobility of resources) attribute of the market.

[19] This disregards the issues of a general equilibrium sort raised by Meade and by Lipsey and Lancaster under the doctrine they denoted the "second best."

include both "pure" and "perfect" characteristics) is found in Richardson's *Information and Investment*.[20] He shows that perfect competition involves invalid assumptions about the information available to firms in such a market. The reference is not to the lack of "technical information" about future developments in technology or in the character of products, problems for firms in all types of markets. But what this knowledge means to a given firm in a perfectly competitive market is not evident. Such a firm's problem can be seen more clearly in the pedantic "market information" cases, such as when demand increases. Obviously the consequent price increase signals that output is deficient and that capacity should be enlarged. But which of the numerous firms in a perfectly competitive market is "nominated" and will or should, rationally, make a capacity response? Because all firms are assumed to be alike the disequilibrium impinges on them equally. There is no information that nominates a particular firm to respond. None may, or, alternatively, most or all may, which would overdo the capacity need.

The frequency of the latter behavior, in response to higher or lower current prices by the competitively structured agricultural industries is well documented by statistical investigations. The year-to-year acreage changes for annual crops and in the longer cycles in the livestock and fruit industries[21] capacity and output show "cobweb" behavior that raises doubts as to whether performance in these industries is socially optimal. If one adds the empirically valid observation that the time span for downward adjustment of capacity is longer (it happens not to be in hog production, the classic case of the cobweb theorem) than for capacity increases, he would see that response to a disequilibrating development forms a still more distorted picture.

In his critique of perfect competition, Richardson plays with a straw man but for a purpose. His purpose is to demonstrate by formal analysis what others have held from observation, that competition (in a looser sense) works well because it is, in fact, imperfect to a significant degree. In the Richardson format, this means that when a

---

[20] G. B. Richardson, *Information and Investment* (Oxford: Oxford University Press, 1960).

[21] For an unusual case, with a careful documentation of the dynamics of adjustment in a fruit industry, see Roy J. Smith, "The Lemon Prorate in Retrospect," *The Journal of Political Economy*, LXIX, December, 1961, pp. 573–586.

disequilibrium occurs in an imperfect market, certain firms can identify themselves as nominated to adjust because, for example, the demand change is primarily by their customers or because the particular factor prices they pay have moved. Signals are given to certain firms and not vaguely to all or to none and, presumably, adjustment will be more orderly. One could go on (Richardson does in part) to examine how uncertainty faced by firms correlates with degree of competitiveness, as defined above, and explore the possible effects on efficiency, a topic to be considered below.

Marshall-Like but Not Fully So

Particularly since the War there has been a vigorous debate between those whose theoretical orientation is the monopolistic-imperfect doctrines and those aligned with a Marshall-like concept of competition and conditions favoring it. Indeed, the latter group's theory would have been denoted the old for the purpose of this paper had not the monopolistic-imperfect competition doctrines been so widely accepted for decades. The members of the school of central interest in this section are very strong supporters of the merits of competition, of its vigor, and of its tendency to undermine monopoly, except where inhibited by government action or assistance. But they do not make the mistake of assuming that this calls for markets that are even close to the purely competitive in structure. For analyzing the performance of markets they fall back on a loose or vague Marshallian concept of competition. Like Marshall, they are concerned primarily with long-run equilibria. They conclude, but have not demonstrated extensively, that most of the individual firm's monopoly power stressed in the "old" theory has minimal influence in the long-run. Marshall seemed less sure of this in successive editions as he worried about his falling supply curve analysis.

Also he recognized that the target toward which long-run tendencies work, shifts frequently and therefore the properties of the long-run equilibrium may not be obtained. Those who now work in this general framework agree that what is observed may in fact be only a series of incomplete adjustments. But they do not grant that competitive markets fail to obtain (or is it do come closer to reaching than do alternative organizing arrangements?) the welfare properties of the long-run competitive equilibria. For example, Stigler says, "I do not believe this [that a succession of unexpected and large disturbances prevent adjustments to long-run equilibria] is true"—but "This is an empirical quesion. . . ." His negative answer[22] is based on a test that is not a convincing method of dealing with D. H. Robertson's often-quoted phrase, "The long run is not of equal length at both ends,"[23] that is, the exit of specialized fixed capital from a particular use is far more prolonged and painful than its entry. Consequently, the school being considered here places no credence in the "Too Much Competition?" suggestion to be dealt with in the next section.

What is confusing is their stand on the identification of and theorizing about markets generally denoted "oligopolistic" which are Chamberlin's major concern. On the one hand, only two types of markets are identified, competitive and monopolistic with the latter defined as, "the firm is the industry."[24] Yet in two footnotes on the same page the fact of oligopoly "as a group of firms producing the same product," is acknowledged and so is the possibility that each of the firms may have a demand curve with elasticity different than that for the product![25] But one does not find in the literature of this school much search for the effect of fewness, combined with other features of the market, on the ability to "agree" by "conjectural independence" or by overt collusion.[26]

Added to the emphasis on the long-run is the employment often of a concept of the market wider than that of Marshall. On the one hand Chamberlin's product marked off by a small degree of differentiation is denoted as methodologically erroneous, or the employment of assumptions because they are descriptively "real."[27] Where there are numerous sellers of such close substitutes—Chamberlin's large numbers case—no significant effect on performance is held to exist in the

---

[22] George J. Stigler, *Capital and Rates of Return in Manufacturing Industries* (Princeton: Princeton University Press, 1963), pp. 56, 64, 65.

[23] Which is a major basis for Joan Robinson's conclusion as to "The Impossibility of Competition," E. H. Chamberlin (ed.), in *Monopoly and Competition and Their Regulation* (London: Macmillan, 1954), pp. 245–54.

[24] Milton Friedman, *Essays in Positive Economics* (Chicago: University of Chicago Press, 1953), p. 35.

[25] *Ibid.*, n. 29, 30.

[26] William Fellner, *Competition Among the Few* (New York: Alfred A. Knopf, Inc., 1949). George J. Stigler, "A Theory of Oligopoly," *Journal of Political Economy*, LXXII, February, 1964, pp. 44–61, does advance hypotheses with respect to some aspects of oligopolistic behavior.

[27] Milton Friedman, *op. cit.*, pp. 15, 34, 36.

long run, a bit of casual empiricism, but of probable validity in large part. A further methodological criticism is that concentration on the behavior of the individual firms thwarts analysis of meaningful groupings of firms into industries or markets so that analyses can stop short of the general equilibrium scope,[28] a criticism accepted de facto by those schooled in the "old theory" when engaged in empirical or policy analysis.[29] As to the scope of such an industry, the economists whose views are being considered, at times go beyond Marshall because a firm's activities can move over a wider field in a few years. While there is considerable empirical evidence of such diversification,[30] that does not mean that the lines added are in the same economic market as were the firm's original activities.

But the use of the three-digit Census industries as the relevant market—how Marshall would have shuddered!—and other features of recent quantitative reports on the origins of concentration, or of its effect on performance, are not convincing. Finding no finer breakdown of expenses and profits of industries in the *Statistics of Income*, Census industries of comparable width are used to measure concentration or to serve as an "index of monopoly."[31] This is not the place to detail the frequency with which these categories are too broad to be denoted industries in a useful sense, nor to indicate the fundamental inconsistencies between income tax data for a corporation as an entity and Census summing of shipments of a three-digit class of products by plants of a company. Beyond these considerations is the assumption of a linear relation between concentration and rates of return, or between advertising expenditures and concentration, over a range from less than ten to very high percentages of volume accounted for by the four largest firms.[32] It is not surprising that no significant relation was found between the degree of concentration in markets so defined and rates of return in the equally wide Bureau

---

[28] *Ibid.*, pp. 38–39.

[29] See p. 197, above.

[30] Michael Gort, *Diversification and Integration in American Industry* (Princeton: Princeton University Press, 1962), pp. 27–64, 100–141.

[31] George J. Stigler, *Capital and Rates of Return in Manufacturing Industries, op. cit.*, pp. 66–67; Lester V. Telser ("Advertising and Competition," *Journal of Political Economy*, LXXII, December, 1964, p. 542), says "Concentration of sales among the four leading firms in industry is a widely accepted measure of monopoly"; and G. Warren Nutter, *The Extent of Enterprise Monopoly in the United States* (Chicago: University of Chicago Press, 1951), pp. 8, 19, 20, adopts concentration ratios as an index of monopoly on pragmatic grounds after having outlined their defects.

[32] With respect to the plausibility of the linearity assumption, see pp. 215–16, below.

of Internal Revenue industries in which all of a firm's profits are assigned to its major line.[33] For a more carefully defined (and narrower than three-digit in most cases) industries Stigler does find a meaningful relationship between high concentration and rates of return.[34] By similarly inappropriate procedures no clear relation was found between concentration and advertising outlays.[35] Nor would such a relationship be expected to be substantial even by use of adequately refined data, for few, if any, economists had assumed that advertising alone, of all the costs of sellers' persuasion, is a significant source of monopoly.

What has not emerged from the work that follows the general viewpoint being considered here is a positive theory that explains the performance of markets that are not near either the clearly competitive or clearly monopolistic poles. That is not to say that there is a lack of concern with these markets. Rather the reference is to the development of hypotheses concerning the structural or other features of a market that appear to explain the performance of such markets, followed by empirical testing of these hypotheses. In other words, one cannot form theory by observing performance, but rather by explaining that performance so that it can be predicated.[36] There has been little regard for the variables found useful in intensive studies of particular markets.[37] In their preference for a shorter route to generalization by means of cross-section studies, the school considered here has by choice or lack of necessary data, not introduced variables that would permit delineating types of market characteristics that others, including the present writer, deem to be relevant for explaining behavior. These are epitomized by entry barriers which encompass far more than the term "free" (absence of artificial barriers) or its lack connotes, as Bain has shown.[38]

The policy stand that correlates with the general stand of econo-

---

[33] Stigler, *Capital and Rates of Return in Manufacturing Industries, op. cit.*, pp. 66–69. The use of wide industries and also the questionable inclusion of all sizes of firms in such industries is one of several reasons why Stigler's findings are not comparable with those of J. S. Bain ("Relation of Profit Rate to Industry Concentration," *Quarterly Journal of Economics*, August, 1951).

[34] Stigler, "A Theory of Oligopoly," *op. cit.*

[35] Telser, *op. cit.*, pp. 542–45.

[36] Such is the burden of Friedman's methodological essay, *op. cit.*, pp. 3–43, as I interpret it.

[37] The case-by-case method does suffer from the long route, not to plausible hypotheses, but to demonstrated generalizations.

[38] Bain, *Barriers to New Competition* (Cambridge: Harvard University Press, 1956).

mists referred to here, but with diversity within the group, is quite different from that of Kaysen and Turner,[39] and unfriendly to much of current antitrust policy as it is being applied. While many owe an intellectual debt to Henry Simon, he held a "limitist" doctrine of maximum market shares, quite unlike that implicit in the theory outlined in this section. Indeed, some would go as far as to hold that there is little unregulated monopoly in the American economy except for overt collusion, labor unions and government-aided areas such as agriculture, and most government efforts in the general area of the Clayton Law and its amendments worsen the performance of the economy, a viewpoint similar to that of Bork and Bowman referred to earlier.[40]

Too Much Competition?

At the opposite pole to what has just been considered are assertions and hypotheses, but not a well-worked-out theory, about the damage from too much *price* competition. The issue has to do with the economic benefits of unlimited price competition when sunk investment in assets of long potential use-life represents a substantial portion of costs, as it does in specialized agriculture, in mining, and in some forms of manufacturing. An illustration, without judging its merits, is the decades-old contention—now with more support among academic economists than earlier—that farmers' efficiency is affected adversely when they experience frequent sharp declines of prices and of gross incomes. One could add to the list the woes of other raw material producers in large-number markets here and abroad, or of small manufacturers whose attempts at collusion in this country have kept the courts busy.

The important questions have to do with the effect of a high degree of gross income uncertainty on whether the optimal ratio of specialized capital to output will be employed and on whether such industries will progress at the optimal rate. Schumpeter lent support to a negative answer.[41] Some economists give a similar answer for

---

[39] Kaysen and Turner, *op. cit.*

[40] Bark and Bowman, *op. cit.*

[41] Schumpeter, *op. cit.*, pp. 87–106. One can infer much of the same from J. Kenneth Galbraith, *American Capitalism: The Concept of Countervailing Power* (Boston: Houghton-Mifflin, 1952), pp. 89–99.

agriculture,[42] for coal mining, and occasionally for certain types of industrial markets.[43] In this format technological advances in coal mining would be deemed possible by the level and stability of the price for coal as influenced by union action.[44] Abroad one finds much support for these views[45] despite the early post-war surge of pro-competitive policy which, except in Britain, seems to be subsiding. But a systematic theory of too much price competition has not been set forth, although segments of it are found in the literature.

The corresponding policy stands range from "forward prices," or price floors with or without output controls, for major farm crops, to the new world-wide coffee agreement, and even to proposals for a rule of reason in the administration of the law on agreements among firms.[46] It should be noted, however, that most economists who support some government interference with agricultural prices are referring only to shorter calendar periods, as for a crop year, and not to the almost two decades (after the War) of holding prices above long-term equilibrium levels.

ELEMENTS OF A REVISED THEORY OF COMPETITION

The four interrelated analytical steps that together constitute the theory of competition are in large part explicit in price theory. Usually price and output determination is analyzed by assuming a

---

[42] D. Gale Johnson, *Forward Prices for Agriculture* (Chicago: University of Chicago Press, 1947), pp. 89, 224–242.

[43] Almarin Phillips, *Market Structure, Organization and Performance* (Cambridge: Harvard University Press, 1962), pp. 36–39; Clark, "Basing Point Methods of Pricing," *Canadian Journal of Economics and Political Science*, November, 1938; and Kaysen, "Basing Point Pricing and Public Policy," *Quarterly Journal of Economics*, XLIII, 1949, pp. 202–205.

[44] It takes little imagination to conclude that the findings of E. L. Christenson's study of "The Impact of Labor Disputes Upon Coal Consumption" (*American Economic Review*, XLV, March, 1955, pp. 79–112) on stability of coal prices under the unions' output "management" explain the ability and willingness of efficient minds to use internal and external finds to carry out the dramatic mechanization of underground mining portrayed in the same author's *Economic Redevelopment in Bituminous Coal* (Cambridge: Harvard University Press, 1962).

[45] E.g., P. F. Cook, "Orderly Marketing of Competition," *The Economic Journal*, Vol. LXXI, September, 1961, pp. 497–511, which criticizes the cancellation by the British Restrictive Practices Court of a minimum price agreement on the grounds that in an industry of fluctuating raw materials' prices, barring agreements means that the survival and profits of firms must depend primarily on skill in anticipating price movements rather than on efficiency in manufacturing.

[46] Phillips, *op. cit.*, pp. 231–242.

type of market, identified by "structure," at one of the poles or at
some point within the purely competitive-purely monopolistic range.
Not much attention is given to what, logically, is the first step,
namely, the determinants of the type of market except for the
economies of scale relative to the size of the market. The analysis
then, explores the interactions of the demand and supply sides and
explains the adjustment processes, the equilibrium tendencies, and
the properties of equilibria. Whether rivalry (or agreement) will
center on price or other parameters of action is only developed in
part. In turn, performance is predicted on the basis of the structure of
the market (with conditions of entry given heavy weight) and the
form rivalry takes or the ease of agreement. What is needed is much
more development of each of these four steps and the interrelations
among them. The result will be a more complex theory[47] which,
among its varied features, may contain non-static elements.

The proposals I shall present have some, but far from full, kinship
to the monopolistic-imperfect competition theory. Much is owed also
to the empirical research and theorizing of industrial organization
economists. Finally, the performance predictions that are implied,
but not the structure of the theory, has much similarity to those of the
"Back to Marshall But Not Fully So" school. My proposals are an
attempt to develop a more complete explanatory system as to what
gives rise to different market organizations, practices, and performance than this school offers. In what follows I have not formulated
systematic propositions and intermix suggestions of variables and of
theoretical structure with comments about empirical plausibility.

The Basic Conditions Surrounding the Market

The first step is to draw a distinction between "basic conditions,"
or determining forces external to the firms—note the plural—in the
industry, and the "organization" of the market. The word "structure"
is confusing for, as ordinarily used; (a) it excludes important features of the organization of the market horizontally and vertically;
and (b) it mixes under the same heading organizational features of

---

[47] The idea of the simplest possible theory, often referred to as the principle of
"Occam's razor," is valid, but it is necessary that it "cut" effectively. The contention
here is that formal price theory has been too general to effectively "cut" with respect to
many markets.

the market, certain of the external basic conditions that presumably shape the market, and the consequences of some market practices. Economies of scale relative to the size of the market is a basic condition that not only influences directly the number and size distribution of sellers but is also a major condition of entry. Product differentiation is a function of the properties of the good, of the demand for it which includes buyers' preferences, and also of the existing size distribution of sellers.

Full development of the basic conditions that are apt to be important for many industries—they make a sizeable list—is beyond the limits of this paper. Among those that are important and widely prevalent are the character of costs, the elasticity and differentiability of demand, the organization of supplying and buying sides (including intermediate buyers down through the distribution trades) of markets in which the firms at a particular transaction level deal, the sources and degree of uncertainty of external origin, and finally certain institutions.

While the implications of basic conditions do not now promise to result in a fully determinate theory of market organization, one can come closer to that goal by this route. Furthermore, from a full exploration of the significance of basic conditions one can gain more understanding of market practices.

The Organization of the Market: Pervasive Heterogeneity

The organization of a market encompasses far more than the number and size distribution of sellers. (In my format the organization and behavior of supplying and buying industries, including consumers, are basic conditions.) Organization clearly includes degree of vertical integration, and the variation among firms in this regard for that will affect reactions to certain disequilibrating events. Similarly firms differ not only in size but in variety of goods sold at a given transaction step and in channel of sale for a given product.

Throughout, one must be wary or, indeed, should expect to find invalid, any such implicit assumption as that firms are alike, or can be considered to be alike for analytical purposes as if created *de novo*. Nor do they compete, or agree, as if all of them were located on one point and sell an identical good to homogeneous customers. Firms as organizations usually differ and so do their "positions" in the market.

They treasure some differences and it would not be rational to attempt to wipe out those they would like to alter (except over an extended period). They do not and cannot behave as if born at this moment for their characteristics and their relations to suppliers and customers, and with rivals, have developed over time in rational reaction to past data, modified by good or bad luck. Nor do they conduct themselves as is assumed in formal theory, that is, as if they were merely focal points played on by factor markets and product demand to which they react as if they were computers with a given "set."[48] On the contrary they are organizations with a survival bias which may contribute to a growth bias and also lead them to limit reliance on external sources of capital.[49]

Typically, for other than crude materials, what can usefully be called a product for most analytical purposes (in the broader Marshallian concept not the narrow Chamberlinian type of "product"), being such a broadly defined product, is not often homogeneous. Whether it is or not, it is not ordinarily sold in a single channel to a single type of customer. The market is segmented for reasons that stem from the basic conditions and history.[50]

Market Practices: Ease of "Agreement" and "Need" to Agree

There is a rational explanation not only of the organization of the market but also of practices in each segment of the market. In large part these reflect the diversity of basic conditions which played on the broad market and on its members in the past, modified by the slow process of adaptation to changes in these conditions. At a given time behavior is restrained powerfully by the very high cross elastici-

---

[48] See R. B. Heflebower, "Stability in Oligopoly," *The Manchester School*, XXXIX, January, 1961, pp. 79–94. In many ways Almarin Phillips' theory of interfirm organization (*op. cit.*, pp. 21–46) is analogous to the argument here except that the latter does not rely on Phillips' contention that the "value systems" of firms differ. On this point my argument is orthodox; given positions various firms occupy in or can achieve in the organization of the market, they find different forms and degrees of competition to be profit maximizing.

[49] The latter bias, stated positively as a preference for growth out of internally generated funds, underlies John Meyer and Edwin Kuh, *The Investment Decision* (Cambridge: Harvard University Press, 1957), and, more specifically, comments on behavior of oligopolists in Chapter XII.

[50] I have not worked in a promising variable, that of the stability of market shares. For a discussion of this topic and references to the literature, see testimony of Lee E. Preston in *"Economic Concentration,"* Hearings of the Senate Sub-Committee on Antitrust and Monopoly, Part I, pp. 56–70, 325, 333 (1964).

ties among firms' products within a segment and, less so in a short calendar period, by the much lower cross elasticities of demand and supply between segments. But these cross elasticities are nearly always experiencing a degree of change because of dynamical or historical developments. For consumer goods, particularly, segments range in character from those quite highly competitive (as defined earlier) by means of price to those where this type of rivalry is nominal and such rivalry as there is fails, in a short calendar period, to meet the test of economic competition. But as these firms struggle among themselves by the best (from their viewpoints) means of non-price competition, not infrequently and as a by-product, they increase the cross elasticity of demand between their segment and others. Furthermore, the level of price in such segments and the responsiveness of their prices to external developments are conditioned by the behavior of adjacent and more (price) competitive segments. Examples include the influence of competitively priced copper scrap on the price of primary copper or of private (distributive) brands of durables or foods on manufacturers' brands.

Non-price competition devices are expensive (selling expenses, costly frequent changes in superficialities of product or package and, for not a few products, expensive distribution methods) and in large part self-defeating for the group. The efforts of each tends to be neutralized by the efforts of the others. Each is, in substance, attempting to mark off a part of the market by selling devices that have a quasi-vertical integrating effect. Advertising to final buyers persuades them to discipline the distributive trades (as has happened fully in tobacco and proprietary drug items) whereby the manufacturers attain a degree of control over retailers as to what they stock and display. For other products, such as automobiles, the dealer becomes *de facto* the representative of one manufacturer. All of this is expensive to the manufacturers or the dealers that represent them, and in some commodity lines invites backstream integration by large retailing companies at least to the extent of taking over the merchandising function under their own brands. This process is often dynamic as will be seen below.

One could go on to sketch other facets of difference among firms and their correlated practices but space limits forbid. What does emerge, particularly had I been able to develop more fully the differing impact of dynamic influences and of historical events on various groups of sellers in markets, is the limited significance of size distribution of firms except when concentration is very high. This can be seen by considering the ease of "agreement" and the "private need" to agree.

One should visualize an index of the degree to which the organization of the market determines the degree of competitive behavior but indexes reflecting size distribution only, such as Herfindahl's, do not help much. Once one considers the problems of agreement among more than a very few firms, compounded by heterogeneity within the product line and among firms, all that he can say with confidence is that concentration has something to do with expected performance. It is then seen as only a *necessary* condition but not a *sufficient* condition for firms to approach joint profit maximization by specified degrees. Surely only high degrees of concentration are apt to be very significant. Even if firms are alike in the attributes referred to above, the effectiveness of conjectural restraint must decline at some sharply *increasing* rate as the number of the firms rises. Add the probability that, with more and more firms, the diversity of their relevant attributes multiplies and the difficulty of agreement is compounded.

We should visualize an index of ease of "agreement" that is derived from a series of variables, some difficult to quantify, whose functional relation to performance we cannot now specify. But we can indicate the potential relevance of some variables (as I have done above) and often the direction of their influence.[51] Very near the duopoly pole the number of firms accounting for a very high percentage of volume would dominate an index of conjectural restraint on independence of action. Two firms could be quite unlike in several features and still reach a joint profit maximizing price "agreement" (subject to the entry restraint) via the conjectural route and quite certainly could do so via formal collusion.[52] But as the number grows an index of the ease of "agreement" would drop off much more rapidly than does the Herfindahl index except, possibly, for a point

---

[51] Stigler, "A Theory of Oligopoly," *op. cit.*, introduces also behavior of different groups of buyers.

[52] Why restrict the analyses to "conjectural" or "quasi-agreement"? An effective formal agreement amounts to establishing a single "multi-firm" with respect to the phases of operation covered by the agreement as reached. The features of a formal agreement and the degree of compliance with it can be expected to reflect, but more perfectly so, the very influences that make agreement via the conjectural route easy or difficult and that affect its properties.

not considered thus far, that of the *private* "need" for agreement. By that "need" I mean the penalty for non-agreement which consists not so much of foregoing profits nearer to joint profit maximization as of the drastic reduction of cash flow by active price competition in the event of a substantial margin of excess capacity. Without expounding fully the character of the need to agree, two influences affecting it are the degree of inelasticity of demand (in a very short calendar period) and the level of the price floor set by the average variable cost. "Need" to agree can, and surely must, tend to offset the declining index of ease of "agreement" as the number of firms and the divergence of interests among them handicap agreement at a price above the short-period competitive level.[53] Inability to "agree," conjecturally, in these circumstances can be expected to have one or more of the following consequences: a concentration trend via survival or merger; the development of practices that restrain price competition; formal collusion; or in the absence of one or more of these, the employment of lower ratios of specialized fixed capital to output.

Only two of these practices will be sketched here. The basing point system, with its price leadership overtone, was designed to perfect the price structure for a commodity and to penalize the price cutter automatically and thereby stabilize the price.[54] In the shoe industry (and also in women's apparel) practices have evolved at the various vertical steps with respect to producing to order or to stock, or carrying specialized inventories, that minimize the uncertainties of volume and style faced by those least able to bear it.[55]

WHAT ABOUT DYNAMICS?

Over the years I have come to the conclusion that there are some quite pervasive dynamic influences on market organization and behavior. In general, these point toward greater social benefit from markets for which the ability to "agree" index is distinctly above the

---

[53] For a more full exposition of the character of these two indexes, see the present author's "Conscious Parallelism and Administered Prices," in *Perspectives on Antitrust Policy*, Almarin Phillips, ed. (Princeton: Princeton University Press, 1965), pp. 107–110.

[54] Kaysen, "Basing Point Pricing and Public Policy," *Quarterly Journal of Economics*, XLII, 1949, pp. 305–311.

[55] For example, see Ruth P. Mack, "Business Expectations and the Buying of Materials," in *Expectations, Uncertainty and Business Behavior* (New York: Social Science Research, 1959), pp. 106–118.

level where unrestrained price competition would prevail than one would predict from monopolistic-imperfect competition theory. Three such influences are: (1) the effect of the extent of price competition in the event of a disequilibrium on the production functions employed; (2) the dynamic consequences of product differentiation in some circumstances; and (3) the conditions under which innovation can be expected.

(1) Enough has been said earlier about industries where optimal efficiency (under static assumptions) requires a high ratio of specialized capital to output to make the situation clear.[56] It is important primarily because, as is usually the case, the demand for the product is highly inelastic (in a short calendar period) and demand (or output in the case of agriculture) is subject to wide and unpredictable variations.

But in formal theory and in most economists' use of it, the assumption is made that, regardless of where a market falls in the competition-monopoly range, the level of firms' cost curves reflects employment of optimal production functions and factor proportions unaffected by uncertainty. But if prices drop as in competitive theory in the event of a substantial margin of excess capacity—note the emphasis on the unfavorable surprise—one avenue of escape costly to the economy is the employment of less capital intensive and efficient production methods. Another device is to integrate vertically into a market (fully or by the semi-integration devices noted earlier) which is more imperfect and prices more stable or where temporary price discrimination will not have explosive consequences. Cases include integration by copper firms into fabrication and semi-integration by petroleum refiners into retailing. But such vertical integration constitutes the major barrier to entry.[57] The contention by some that futures markets can provide adequate opportunity to shift uncertainty by contract I find wholly unconvincing for the problem considered here.

(2) For goods that are sufficiently different to be denoted "new" and whose introduction constitutes innovation, the role of differentiation may be dynamic. It is the effective instrument for developing demand for the new product. But the success of the innovator and

---

[56] The literature on this point is extensive but scattered. Richardson, *op. cit.*, pp. 88–101, comments on this point.

[57] Bain, *Barriers to New Competition*, *op. cit.*, pp. 212, 216, 217.

that of his imitators in developing consumer demand along with improvement in the functional properties of the good tends to undermine the high degree of differentiation the innovating firm(s) had achieved. Differentiation devices also teach consumers or at least build their confidence in the want-satisfying properties of the good. Progressively the "specialty becomes a commodity" that enters most families' expenditure plans. The door is then open for sellers whose appeal is a lower price. These entrants establish lower-price market segments and benefit from the increasing cross elasticity of demand between what they sell and the pioneers' well-known brands. The effects on some combination of the latters' price and market share is obvious. This dynamic aspect of competition has been of unusual significance in the past few decades in this country.[58]

(3) Now I come to the potential dynamic aspect of competition that is the most difficult to expound and the least developed in theory; the behavior of oligopolists estopped from price competition. Obviously I am not referring to an oligopoly for which an effective and enforceable price and quota agreement is preferred and possible. Within the limits of such an agreement the oligopoly becomes a multi-firm but the dynamic force referred to above and in what follows may affect the provisions of or undermine the agreement. In the absence of an effective formal agreement an oligopolistic firm can turn in one of two directions. One is aggressive product differentiation of which no more will be said here.

Of far greater importance is the potential diversion of the firm's attention toward research and innovation and the degree to which it will act independently (compete) by doing so.[59] With respect to process innovation Lange[60] concluded that oligopolists will act independently in developing and in using factor-saving innovations. But output-increasing ones would be adopted only if the expected cost saving were enough to make profits (adjusted for uncertainty) after

---

[58] This process is described formally (but not in a dynamic framework) and tested for one new good, by Demsetz, "Product Innovation and Imitation" (unpublished doctoral thesis at Northwestern University, 1959).

[59] I am not dealing here with the relation of the size of the firm and of a substantially less than purely competitive market organization on the capacity to innovate. See Edwin Mansfield, "Size of Firm, Market Structure, and Innovation," *Journal of Political Economy*, LXXXI, December, 1963, pp. 556–576.

[60] Oscar Lange, "A Note in Innovations," *Review of Economic Statistics*, XXXV, 1943, pp. 19–25.

a new equilibrium had been established, to be clearly higher than prior to the disturbance. But this is static and stationary analysis; in a growing market the innovator is in a position to obtain a higher share of the added than of the earlier capacity. Rivalry in capacity expansion and in cost reduction among members of a cartel has been observed frequently, with the agreement collapsing unless the expanding, low-cost firm gets a larger share.

Product innovations (not considered by Lange) are inherently disturbing if they are quite close substitutes for what rivals sell.[61] But there are several reasons for expecting independent action in product innovation. Volume does not ordinarily shift to the innovator as rapidly as it would to an unmatched price cutter. Rivals would not be expected to react as violently, and when they do the reaction is apt to be a product change, which takes months or years to execute. In the meantime the successful innovator obtains substantial short-term profits and often a long-term benefit in the form of buyers' enhanced preference for other items he sells.

By no means is the proportion of successes high—clearly not as high as in process innovation[62]—but careful study of the product and of the market for it adds information and increases the innovator's confidence in it.[63] Presumably the innovating firm would have more information and be less uncertain about the new product's prospects than would be a rival picked at random. Given such differential knowledge and expectations of firms, holding back on one firm's part gives it no assurance that rivals will do likewise.

Desisting from innovation in an era of rapid developments in the basic sciences and of application to industrial use is unlikely. No firm or group of firms can be certain what type, by whom, and when an upsetting innovation will occur. Making a substantial investment in research as an information-getting device will minimize the chances of surprises by rivals and maximize the ability to imitate or "innovate around" an innovational surprise. All of this must lead to decisions on the basis of a relatively short planning horizon. Prospective profit rates per year must be higher to encourage investment. The impor-

---

[61] See the paper in this volume by Almarin Phillips with respect to the effects of substitution between the old and the new products on oligopolists' willingness to innovate by means of the latter.

[62] See the investigations reported by Charles F. Carter and Bruce R. Williams in *Investment in Innovation* (Oxford: Oxford University Press, 1958), pp. 88–107.

[63] A firm's own research and development staff has this effect (*ibid.*), pp. 67–69.

tant point is, however, that the "value" of the *status quo* in the eyes of each firm must encourage it to act quite independently in product innovations.

Finally because firms in concentrated industries are usually estopped from primarily relying on price competition and find the potential results of research to be the most feasible independent course of action, the rate of technological advance will occur at the optimum pace, whether it is of exogenous or endogenous origin, and that its occurrence is not uniquely affected by the organization of the market. Much of the literature of the institutional-empirical sort, on the other hand, has emphasized the sleepy monopolist or oligopolist whose contentment includes lazy technology. Schumpeter challenged this view as to both the willingness and the ability of oligopolistic firms to innovate but he did not develop a model of favorable conditions for innovation in few-firm industries. What has been sketched above suggests some components of such a model, but they are not set forth as formal propositions.

DECISION-MAKERS "ENDS" AND COMPETITION

All of the preceding has been quite orthodox in that some concept of profit maximization by firms was assumed. I will not explore the doubts (on formal grounds) about the meaning and usefulness of that concept once uncertainty becomes a significant aspect of decision-making. Instead, I raise the question about whether the sales or growth maximization hypotheses recently expounded as the goal of management-controlled corporations can be expected to affect market performance. So far there has not been a systematic empirical demonstration of whether these hypotheses provide better explanations of observed behavior than does profit maximization. There have been no more than casual observations (as by Baumol[64]) or a deduction from the levels of autonomy of managements that are nevertheless subject to important restraints (as in Marris[65]). It is equally plausible that firms judge a lower-price policy and aggressive-growth policy to be a more certain route to long-term

[64] William J. Baumol, *Business Behavior Value and Growth* (New York: Macmillan Co., 1959), pp. 45–82.

[65] Robin Marris, "A Model of Management Enterprise," *Quarterly Journal of Economics*, May, 1963.

profit maximization.[66] Businessmen know the uncertainties accompanying a high-profit policy; they really do not know the level of the entry-limit price, or of the price at which rivals' indirect or direct price-cutting will start. Unfortunately, both Baumol and Marris analyze the decision-making oligopolist without regard to his rivals' past or possible future behavior.

If a sales or growth maximizing firm, placed in its market environment, does behave differently than it would by carefully defined profit-maximizing criterion, the effect must be more independent use of whichever device of rivalry is judged to be most effective. Sales cost curves can be expected to rise (to the right) more quickly than do production cost curves and, indeed, often results in a mutually neutralizing rivalry and higher level of costs. It is quite possible that rivalry will be channeled not only into product change but also into diversification into other and rapidly growing industries. Gort's findings indicate firms' wide use of the latter avenue of growth,[67] which amounts to established-firm entry into growth industries with the effect of augmenting competition there.

CONCLUDING COMMENTS

The "old" theory had formal elegance, except when faced with the oligopoly problem, but it is not of demonstrated comparable utility. Its defects stem primarily from its static character and its reliance on a simple view of market structure. At the one pole, it could be and has been used to predict results of some markets that are highly competitive organizationally, but comparable predictive power will be found for markets faced by uncertainty of gross revenue combined with slow exit of excess resources. Lack of more findings about such markets stems from the fact that few outside of agriculture have these sources of uncertainty are also highly competitive organizationally. In the industrial sector, where fewness of sellers is present in most markets but very few in only some, failure of the theory reflects not merely the lack of a definitive theory of oligopoly. Much of the trouble reflects also the fact that the price theory is built on the concept of clearly separate markets, within which there is homogeneity of product and of firms. Blurred market limits and heterogene-

---

[66] As E. G. Nourse argued in *Price Making in a Democracy* (Washington: Brookings Institution, 1946), pp. 147–226.

[67] Gort, *op. cit.*, pp. 111–127.

ity inside markets are not merely different data, they also demand a more complex set of analytical variables for some important purposes at least. Even had such a complex theory been developed, of the traditional static sort, it would not be adequate. In substantial degree oligopoly-like markets tend to be disturbed by behavior that probably can be analyzed only in a dynamic framework. Even the theory of entry, which has made so much progress lately, falls short, for *potential* entry into oligopoly involves estimates of the future about which both established firms and potential entrants have different views and degrees of confidence in their estimates.

In a sense the deficiencies of price theory are dated. It was more useful decades ago than now to the degree that market organization and behavior reflect, or are in a state of flux because of, the high ratios of specialized fixed capital to output of today and the widespread door-opening advances in the basic sciences. Important is the watchful eye of government for agreements and other practices that inhibit independence of action by firms.

These conclusions, by no means, support a major slackening of an alert antitrust policy, particularly for an easy-going stand on mergers.[68] If the forces leading to independence of action by firms are as potent as I think they are, they represent opportunities for and rewards for firms who are the very ones whose investment moves can be accomplished by building. One cannot support much of the language of and the expression of pressing social need to block mergers *under the facts* of the Brown Shoe case, nor some provisions and more of the enforcement of the Robinson-Patman Act. But these actions are not the major danger to a competitive market system. What is more alarming is a general faith in the everywhere pervasiveness of competition except when blocked by collusion. Indeed, this view ends up in the embarrassing stand of approving agreement by conjectural restraints on price competition, possibly only where sellers are very few and much of their rivalry is by socially expensive practices, while condemning the generally less effective formal collusion among 30 or 50 small manufacturers. Such is the Bork and Bowman stand referred to earlier.

---

[68] The author has spelled out the rationale for a quite rigorous policy with respect to mergers (compared to the much lesser concern about present market structures implicit above), in "Corporate Mergers: Economic Analyses and Policy," *Quarterly Journal of Economics*, LXXVII, November, 1963, pp. 537–538.

A *marketing view of patents and competition is presented by Wroe Alderson.* He *points out that the patent system performs a function in the marketing of inventions and says that what the patentee generally receives is not a true monopoly right but a chance to become established in competition.* As *to the competitiveness of an industry over time, he suggests that it would increase as the number of expired patents gain in preponderance over patents in force.* He *further suggests that maintenance of competition through encouraging entry and survival of new firms might be more rewarding than the more negative approach often taken.*

WROE ALDERSON was Professor of Marketing at the Wharton School of Finance and Commerce, University of Pennsylvania, and Chairman of the Advisory Board of its Management Science Center. He studied at George Washington University, the University of Pennsylvania, and Massachusetts Institute of Technology. He was past president of the American Marketing Association, founder of the management consulting firm, Alderson Associates, and a member of the Operations Research Society of America and the Institute of Management Science. His publications include *Marketing Behavior and Executive Action, Theory in Marketing,* 1st ed., with Reavis Cox, *Marketing and the Computer* with Stanley Shapiro and *Planning and Problem Solving in Marketing* with Paul Green.

CHAPTER 12

A MARKETING VIEW OF
THE PATENT SYSTEM

Wroe Alderson

Many years ago I spent a few months in the Patent Office in my
first job as a government clerk. These months were pleasant and
uneventful except for a remark I chanced to overhear. A new
Commissioner or Deputy Commissioner was being shown through
the place and stopped near my desk to say that he had all he could
possibly absorb for the day. "There is one thing," he said, "that no
man could possibly invent. That is the Patent Office itself as it stands
today. It is so complicated that it just had to grow."

Before we abolish the Patent Office as at least one economist—Seymour Melman—proposes, we had best reexamine its operations to be
doubly sure that we can get along without it. It stands today as the
culmination of a long process of growth and adaptation. Once it was
gone, only a towering genius of organization could recreate it over
night.

The attempt here is to provide a new perspective by presenting a
marketing view of the patent system. Marketing is the grubby
country cousin of economics which pokes around in the soil of
human behavior looking for the roots of marketing processes and
institutions. Marketing is firmly based in the ecology of operating
systems and its stock in trade is descriptive protocols of the way a
system functions. Sometimes this study of how a system works results
in recommendations of how to make it work better. Marketing
studies have brought about major improvements in the marketing
plans of individual firms, but they have also led to better marketing
for entire industries.

225

Dr. Fritz Machlup has taken the measure of the knowledge industry in the United States, accounting for roughly 30 percent of gross national product in 1959. Some of the end products of the knowledge industry need to be marketed. Among these are the technical ideas which are produced by inventors and, in some cases, incorporated in salable products. The patent system performs a function in the marketing of inventions. Our program is to consider whether this function is performed efficiently and, if possible, to point out opportunities for improvement.

A market is made by the confrontation of buyers and sellers. The first task of the marketing view is to identify suppliers and customers in the market for technical ideas. It demonstrates its utility even at this level by clearing up some apparent contradictions. Some industries are vigorous defenders of the patent system. Other industries regard patents as an unavoidable nuisance or judge their total effect to be positively harmful. Is there any logical reason why the drug and chemical industry should be pro-patent and the automobile industry should be indifferent or anti-patent? Was the prevailing attitude of the automobile industry shaped by the historical accident of Henry Ford's defiance of the Selden patent?

The paradox is resolved as soon as we correctly identify the parties at interest. The drug and chemical manufacturers do not correspond to the automobile manufacturers in their use of patents but to the manufacturers of automobile parts. The parts manufacturer uses patents where he can to differentiate his product. He backs the patent system just as enthusiastically as the drug and chemical manufacturer. He is making specific components which the car manufacturer will combine with other components in assembling a car. The drug and chemical manufacturers are making specific materials which will be combined with other materials in patient treatment or industrial processes. They use patents where they can to differentiate their products. It is safe to say that every industry, broadly defined, contains firms which base their product differentiation, and hence their market position, on patents granted or applied for.

The automobile manufacturer does not base the differentiation of his product on individual components. Instead he selects components from a variety of possibilities and tries to create a favorable image for his automobile as a whole. Differentiation is accomplished through strategic choices among technical alternatives and through annual styling. So far as parts are concerned, the car manufacturer is a buyer rather than a seller, since he is essentially an assembler of parts. As a buyer he does not press for product differentiation among parts but is supremely concerned about the differentiation of his own end-product, the completed automobile. What he demands as a

Producer Seeking Differentiation	Buyer Seeking Standardization of Materials or Components
Automotive Parts Producer	Automobile Assembler
Prescription Drug Manufacturers	Hospital and Medical Specialists
Synthetic Fiber Producer	Garment Manufacturer
Producers of Computer Components	Computer Manufacturers
Manufacturers of Synthetic Detergents	Supermarket Chains

purchaser of parts is various degrees of product standardization. Often he requires that he be licensed to make a component as a condition for buying some of these components from the holder of the patent. It is essential, of course, that parts manufactured internally or from outside sources be standardized so that they can be used interchangeably. In producing parts for repairs and replacement the parts manufacturer is also constrained by strict requirements as to product standardization. The need for standardization and interchangeability are extended still further when more than one manufacturer uses a component in his car.

This difference in attitude between seller and buyer is not peculiar to the automobile industry. In fact, there is a well-nigh universal tendency for the seller to seek to differentiate his product, if possible, and for the buyer to want a standard product from several sources. One side endeavors to decrease substitutability and the other side tries to increase it. The effort to make a product distinctive and the counter pressure for standardization can be illustrated simply by identifying seller and buyer in several different fields.

A central thesis of this paper is that both sides need the patent system or something like it even though the need is more obvious from the viewpoint of the seller who is trying to differentiate his product. Disclosure serves not only the rival who may want to appropriate an idea after a lapse of 17 years but the investor who is interested in financing the production of a patented product. The patent files of many large companies are as complete in their specialized fields of interest as those of the Patent Office itself. This is true of automobile manufacturers who are reputedly indifferent to the patent system. Incidentally, the automobile industry still accounts for one-sixth of all the patents issued, having reached a peak in the 20's of nearly one-fourth of all patents.

The manufacturer of computers or automobiles has several primary options when he observes that a patent has been issued in his field of interest. He can buy the product from the company holding the patent. He can buy the patent rights for cash or in exchange for stock participation. He can seek a license to make the product. He can attempt to invent around it. He can appropriate the idea and dare the holder of the patent to sue. All of these things happen, but whichever option is exercised, the value of the initial disclosure to the prospective user is evident.

A patent puts all and sundry on notice of the inventor's claim to a technical idea. This disclosure may happen years before the inventor or the company which undertakes to manufacture the product has any marketing machinery for effective communication with prospective buyers. Meanwhile the files of the Patent Office stand as a running history of the state of the art. Each patent also stands as the initial offer of the product on the market addressed to all and sundry who may either wish to buy the product or make a deal to produce it themselves. The patentee had struck a bargain with his government whereby it will give him a measure of protection in his attempts at effective market entry in return for disclosure.

The basic marketing function performed by the patent system is idea identification. The patent system serves only in the initial stages of the process, since idea identification is a large part of what is going on in any sustained and aggressive marketing program. Idea identification can serve the needs of either the buyer or seller. It is an essential first step toward either product differentiation or product standardization. Identity is the more fundamental logical notion underlying both heterogeneity and homogeneity. We must start with the identity of A to determine either that A is different from B or that A_1 is the same as A_2. The seller is often obliged to talk out of both sides of his mouth, urging the unique qualities of his product on the one hand, and its conformity to fixed standards on the other. The National Association of Purchasing Agents exerts continuous pressure for the standardization of products but its individual members are also on the alert for anything new and different.

What is the legal and economic significance of a patent? Dr. Machlup examines four principal alternatives for justifying the grant of a patent and finds flaws in all four lines of reasoning. The conception here is that the patent system represents one stage in the marketing of technical ideas. It may or may not be the best way of performing this marketing function, but it happens to be the way we do it now. The inventor, like anyone else with something to sell, is subject to all the hazards of the market place. The doctrine of natural rights to ideas as property is scarcely consistent with our American emphasis on the maintenance of competition. Competitive markets offer no guarantee of monopoly profits as a reward for the inventor's ingenuity and toil, since a patent is only one ingredient in market success and an ingredient which is not always essential.

The great majority of independent inventors never realize any net return for their inventions. They may be moved by a hope of profit, but their motivations are at least as complex as those of the run-of-mine citizen who invents nothing at all. When Orville Wright took off at Kitty Hawk the most likely reward was the negative one of breaking his neck. Years later he wondered how he could have been so foolhardy as to make this first flight. The poverty which many noted inventors have endured and inflicted on their families can scarcely be explained by visions of rolling in wealth in later years. The poverty of an indigent inventor is the poverty of a man with a passion and bears a remarkable resemblance to the poverty of a poet or painter.

Whether an inventor receives anything for his effort at all usually depends on various people besides himself who in turn must meet the test of the market. His patent may turn out to be commercially worthless, but it may only appear to be so because of failures in production, finance or marketing. The independent inventor may turn out to be a competent executive in the innovating firm but more often he has no part in it. Frequently he is regarded as a crank or a monomaniac and his business judgment is suspect. Occasionally a Leonardo da Vinci, a Salomon de Coux or a John Logie Baird is so far ahead of the technology of his time that he could scarcely have harbored any illusions about profits from his inventions. The hired inventor is not obliged to meet the test of the market in the short run, for he is paid in advance for what he may eventually create. He is reasonably sure of tenure at least until he presents his first invention.

To define the issuance of a patent as a government grant of a monopoly right is contrary to the commonsense meaning of the term monopoly. In theory he may enjoy a monopoly but he will not enjoy it much if it only means that he has the sole right to make something nobody wants or which he never learns how to market, particularly in the case of the independent inventor. Aside from the fact that the commercial value of his invention is problematical, the effect of the patent is to give him a chance to become established in competition. There are always other ways of satisfying a given need unless the invention is a very remarkable one indeed. It is elementary that the invention, if it provides a new means of satisfaction, must enter into competition with established products. Examples will illustrate the point.

A recent invention with which I have had some contact is a device for handling PERT planning or critical path scheduling. I have advised the inventor and his partner on sundry matters and, in fact, christened the device the "Planalog." Their little company, financed on a shoestring, found itself competing with IBM, Sperry-Rand, RCA, Control Data Corporation and the entire array of multi-million dollar computer manufacturers. Their competitors took no aggressive action against them and, in fact, were hardly aware of their existence. The power of competition was expressed through the common conviction of planners and operations researchers that the only sensible way to do critical path scheduling is on a large-scale computer. After two years this enterprising pair is still solvent and is selling Planalogs at a sufficient rate so that they can pay themselves modest salaries. But the achievement of monopoly is still light years away, even in the highly specialized field of critical path scheduling. All that Mr. Mendell received when the government granted him a patent on the Planalog was a promise of protection for a limited period in his efforts to enter the market.

The case is not essentially different for large companies on patents assigned to them by their engineers and chemists. I served for some years as a marketing consultant on two Monsanto inventions. The first was the product "All," the first low-sudsing detergent. For year the big "soapers" did not feel at all threatened. They counted on the housewife's unshakable illusion that plenteous suds have something to do with cleaning. The market factors changed because of the predominance of the automatic washing machine and the established competitors countered with their own low sudsers. When Monsanto sold "All" to Lever Brothers they were only beginning to break even. To put a new product into the highly competitive synthetic detergent field was a major merchandising achievement, but the product never attained a monopoly position. Even before the other low-sudsing detergents such as "Dash" came into the field "All" had plenty of competition since many consumers continued to use the regular detergents such as "Tide" in their automatic washing machines. The only thing worth monopolizing is a field of use which is not always limited by the physical form of the product. The government has now dropped the charge that the acquisition of "All" by Lever Brothers tended to promote monopoly. The original charge was based on a broad definition of detergents which ignored the distinction between low-sudsing and high-sudsing detergents.

Once again it seems clear that all the patentee received was limited market entry protection. He was only one of the suppliers competing for a place in the family wash even though he only could offer the presumed advantages of washing clothes with a low sudsing detergent. It is characteristic of monopolistic competition that a number of competitors offer to perform the same function, each claiming that his product is different and therefore best. Triffin pointed to what might be called the Chamberlinian paradox. He stated that the concept of an industry was essential to Chamberlin's analysis but that the notion of differentiated monopoly led to an unbounded collection of single firm industries. Surely there is no practical difficulty in reinstating the concept of a broader grouping. An industry is nothing more nor less than a group of firms who are jointly and deliberately engaged in the effort to differentiate their products from each other. Neither Mr. Mendell nor Monsanto were confused about the industries they were trying to enter or their need for some temporary protection if they were to make a successful entry into the market.

The other Monsanto invention was known as Krillium. This was no seeming triviality such as removing the suds from soap. Krillium would change the structure of soil almost instantly and the laboratory demonstrations were most dramatic. It was touted as the scientific marvel of the day and there was talk of reclaiming unproductive soils at home and abroad. A rash of soil conditioners came into existence a year or two after Krillium was announced, but all soon fizzled out. Krillium was a failure, too. I overestimated the market and I had only one lame excuse. My estimate was much smaller than the most pessimistic estimates inside the company. In retrospect it seemed that there were insuperable obstacles to its success, but at the time we were perhaps all a little hypnotized by faith in technological advance. For nearly a year Monsanto was the only producer of a soil conditioner, thus enjoying a very unprofitable monopoly. The product is still manufactured in small quantities for special uses, but I suspect that the company has never recovered the costs of research and product introduction.

The two remaining examples are from the field of electrical appliances. First is the electric can opener patented by General Electric. To some this contraption represents the last word in household decadence. Most housewives have given up doing their own canning and now there are some who disdain the manual opening of their store-bought cans. On the other hand, a few have been heard to remark that the electric can opener is their most prized small appliance. Yet General Electric does not enjoy a monopoly in this field unless the word is given a very narrow and specialized meaning. Millions of conventional can openers are still produced, to say nothing of a number of patented devices which stop short of electrification. General Electric has plenty of competition in appliances for opening cans and does not exercise monopoly control over the field of use. Now suppose that there was a second type of electric can opener in the field and General Electric chose to acquire the producing company. It is likely that the Department of Justice would proceed against General Electric, exercising its option to adopt the narrow definition of the product field instead of the broad definition adopted in the case of Lever Brothers and "All."

And now, at last, the ultimate breakthrough the world has been waiting for—the electric toothbrush! Here there is no question of monopoly since the market is already shared by a number of manufacturers. There has been a mad rush to enter the field like prospectors staking out claims in a gold rush. One or two people were electrocuted while using the first models which were plugged directly into a power line. Innovation took a temporary setback but all of the makes in use today are battery powered. Before we conclude that this invention is downright silly, we should listen to the parents who say that for the first time they can persuade their children to brush their teeth regularly.

All of these inventions illustrate the fact that the patentee receives only a limited market entry protection and even this is tenuous and uncertain. In the past patents have been made the instruments of monopoly but only after they have gone through an initial stage of establishing their commercial values. The Sherman Act was directed substantially against the patent pools which were prevalent at the turn of the century. It was the patents held in trust which were a principal target of the trust busters. Only by pooling all the patents which represent different ways of performing the same function can a company or an industry exercise monopoly control over a field of use. It is egregious error to assume that a patent confers an instantaneous and inevitable monopoly position on the patentee. The marketing effect of an invention patent is utterly unlike that of the letters patent of an earlier day which conferred sole right to market salt or tobacco.

The first hypothesis posed in the current study was derived from J. M. Clark. The late exponent of workable competition theorized that the struggle for differential advantage was marked by rhythmic fluctuations. The innovator first attained an initial advantage which thereafter was neutralized or steadily eroded away. This hypothesis must now be abandoned or greatly modified in its application to patents. The Clark hypothesis does not give adequate weight to the difficulties of entry. In the typical case the new or improved product goes through a long period of gaining ground and only then possesses an advantage which may be eroded away by still newer products. There is a rise and fall of differential advantage, an ebb and flow rather than a sudden creation followed by a protracted period of decline.

Possibly more fruitful are conjectures about factors influencing the competitiveness of an industry over time. Some of these appear to be inevitable trends. Others can be the subject of policy decisions. The first of the inevitable trends is certain to contribute to potential competition in the long run. Suppose that an industry emerged in 1860, the year that the patent period was first standardized at 17 years. At the end of the first 17 years patents began to expire and the ideas once protected began to pass into the public domain. Suppose further, for illustration, that there are just 100 patents each year. At the end of 34 years 1,700 patents would have expired just equalling the 1,700 still in force. Thereafter the preponderance of expired patents might be expected to increase year by year. Potential competition is increased simply by the passage of time.

One mark of maturity in an industry would be the date when the free technology represented by patents first began to exceed in number of items those still under patent. Obviously the count of patents is only a rough measure but patents expired would include the more basic patents in the mature field of technology. The maturity date would never arrive in an industry if patents grew at a geometric rate. If patents in each successive 17-year period were at least twice as great as in the previous period, the patents in force would always exceed the number expired. The date of maturity as defined would come later in some fields than in others, but in no case would it be indefinitely postponed. Growth at the exponential rate assumed would soon pass the limits of possibility. The entire population would consist of inventors and patent examiners for a brief time before the system blew up. The fact is, the total number of patents issued leveled off some years ago. The same thing must have happened in one field after another some time after an initial spurt in inventive activity.

The validity of these assumptions has been tested for invention patents as a whole and for several separate areas of technology. For all patents the hypothesis is confirmed with patents expired at about 1,500,000 running well ahead of patents in force of about 700,000. Patents expired first exceeded patents in force in 1907. The two trend lines were plotted on a logarithmic scale in Chart 12–1. After a dip in the issuance of patents during the decade 1940 to 1950, corresponding to the war and early postwar years, the trend turned upward again in about 1955. It is unlikely that patents in force will ever catch up again to patents expired unless there was some basic change in patent office procedure on the definition of patentability.

Since the assumption about expired patents in relation to patents in force is true in a substantial way, it must be true for most of the

CHART 12–1

ALL INVENTION PATENTS
EXPIRED AND IN FORCE

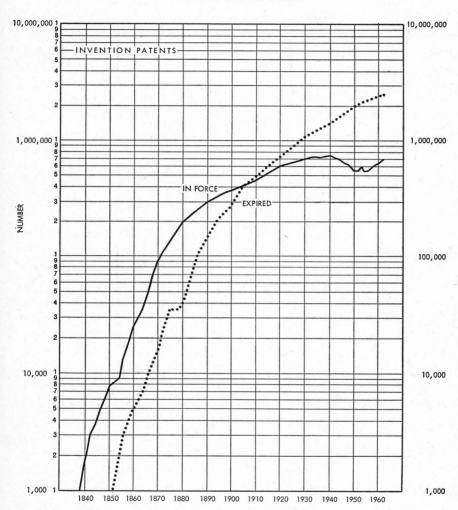

leading classifications. The same comparison has been made for a number of classifications which were selected because patents seemed to play an important part in marketing these products. Very complex products such as automobiles and computers were excluded. In some of these fields the hypothesis was confirmed that the relation of the trend lines were much the same as for all patents. These charts will not be reproduced here but the fields were soaps and detergents, breakfast cereals, tobacco, and automotive tires and wheels. The cross-over dates at which expired patents began to exceed patents in force were as follows: detergents, 1883; cereals, 1930; tobacco, 1896; and tires, 1930.

There are some peculiarities in trends for these groups which are worth noting. From about 1900 to 1942 the gap between detergent patents expired and patents in force was narrowing but the lines never recrossed. They came quite close together during the 1930's and 1940's with the upward surge of invention in synthetic detergents. The gap continues to widen in tobacco also except for an upward surge in patents in force culminating in 1940. Machinery patents are especially important in the tobacco classification but also product patents such as filter tips for cigarettes. In tires and wheels patents in force started a precipitate decline about 1920 with a moderate upturn starting in 1950.

The real surprise was to find several fields in which the trend lines had crossed and recrossed several times. The most spectacular variations observed are those which occurred in prescription drugs. Patents expired first went ahead in 1857, fell below patents in force only four years later, while patents expired took the lead again in 1889. These trends are shown in Chart 12–2. Note that patents in force had a major peak in 1872 and then underwent a precipitate decline until 1908. At this point the number of patents in force was only about 10 percent of the patents expired. There has been a tremendous upsurge in patents ever since, marking the advance in medical science. While the trend for patents in force has not recrossed that for patents expired, it now stands at more than 90 percent of patents expired.

Similar fluctuations have occurred in two other classifications studied. One of these groups is gas-charged beverages. After some early instability the trend for patents expired went ahead again in 1884, apparently for good. There have been extreme fluctuations since that time in patents in force, but it does not appear likely that the trend lines will cross again. Finally there is the classification of prepared flours which rather surprisingly shows an extreme of instability. Patents expired has gone ahead twice, once in 1892 and again in 1928. The trend in patents in force is currently moving up so fast that it may conceivably take the lead again.

CHART 12–2

ETHICAL DRUGS
PATENTS IN FORCE AND PATENTS EXPIRED

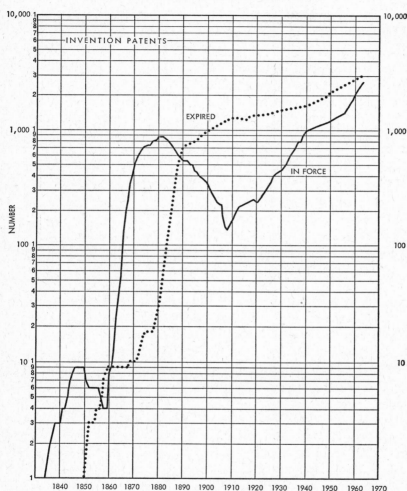

A special study was also made of the percentage of patents issued to individuals, corporations and government. There is a widespread impression that the individual has been almost entirely replaced by the corporation as a source of patents. Chart 12–3 shows that while there has been a trend in that direction it has by no means run its course. In 1900 the percentage of patents issued to individuals was more than four times as great as those issued to corporations. In 1932

CHART 12–3

Percent of Total Invention Patents Issued to
Individuals, Corporations, or Government

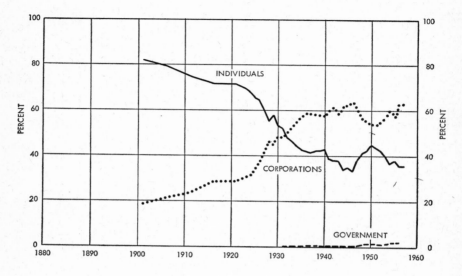

the two types of patentees were equal in number. In 1957 nearly one-third of all patents were still issued to individuals although government now began to show up with 2 percent of the patents issued. Thus there is still a very substantial portion of patents going to individuals and the trend for the future is somewhat doubtful since the downward trend was interrupted by an upward surge which peaked in 1950.

Again the chart for drug patents shows a sharply contrasting picture. Patents issued to individuals or corporations were of equal number in 1929 but the trend for individuals has been steadily downward since and in 1963 was only slightly above 10 percent. Before 1896 nearly 100 percent of medicine patents were issued to individuals year after year, but the trend changed abruptly thereafter. The new trend toward ethical specialties has largely eliminated the individual inventor in the medical field. There would appear to be overriding issues of public policy in the drug field transcending any objective of nurturing and protecting the individual inventor. (Chart 12–4)

CHART 12–4

PERCENT OF "MEDICINE" PATENTS ISSUED TO
INDIVIDUALS, CORPORATIONS, OR GOVERNMENT

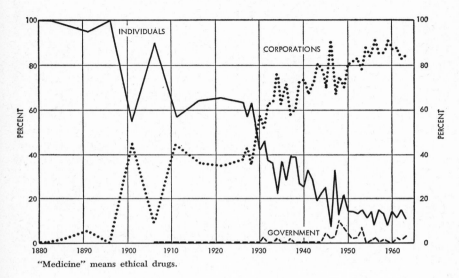

"Medicine" means ethical drugs.

No more charts of this type will be reproduced but a few additional fields will be characterized as bearing closest resemblance to total patents or drug patents. The fields in which the individual inventor still has a significant position include resilient tires and wheels, tobacco, and sewing machines. The sewing machine classification has been an obsession with the independent inventor for many years. Being one of the most complicated mechanical devices ordinarily found in a home, many amateurs have doubtless pondered improvements as they watched their wives seated at a sewing machine. Corporations became equally numerous with individuals in 1906 and the relative position of the individual has suffered further declines since to a little over 20 percent. In addition to drugs, the independent inventor is almost out of the field in detergents, cereals and television.

Government patents have shown up in odd places in recent years to judge by the small sample of classifications. Government does not appear to have taken out any patents in the sewing machine or tobacco groups. There has been government activity in all of the other groups mentioned, including drugs, cereals, television, detergents, and resilient tires and wheels. There was an odd spurt in government patents in cereals during the 1950's. Other than that the trend which might be the greatest cause for concern was in the drug industry. There was an upward trend in patents issued to government for a few years, reaching a peak of over 10 percent of all drug patents in 1948. Since that time this trend has shown a sharp decline.

One of the trends which has been indicated is away from the independent inventor and toward the hired inventor. The term hired inventor is not intended to be invidious but is used only for convenience. On the average, they are far better trained than the independents and soon acquire a depth of specialization in particular product fields. On the average there is a better chance that their inventions will turn out to have commercial value. The hired inventor is a true professional working in a well-equipped laboratory, with ample funds to finance his experiments. But authorities such as Floyd Vaughan say that the hired inventor is chiefly concerned with a number of modest improvements building on an established base. The independent inventor, he says, is generally the source of real breakthroughs even though the great majority of his inventions turn out to be without commercial value. However, the independent inventor tends to disappear altogether when a technical field becomes so complex as medical science or electronics. The independent inventor can no longer provide the minimum resources for making advances in these fields. Breakthroughs can still be expected, however, from scientists working in university laboratories.

The preoccupation of the hired inventor with step-by-step improvements calls for some checking, but Vaughan's statement seems reasonable on the face of it. It needs to be tempered by taking account of acceleration in the marketing of new products and in the constant search for something still newer. Manufacturers are impelled to extend their product lines in order to spread their market risks. A diversified product line is likely to include two contrasting types of products. One class consists of well established products which are currently profitable. The other class includes the newer products which have not yet returned the costs of research and development or perhaps are not yet breaking even on current sales. These products are carried at a loss because they are expected to become profitable at some later time. Some of these products will replace established products now in current demand. Nevertheless the manufacturer has no recourse but to continue to innovate because of pressures from competition and from the market.

Innovation and Antitrust Policy

The device of the government granting patents to itself is relatively new in most classifications, although it began as early as 1906 in the drug industry. The government is not in this instance rewarding an independent inventor or encouraging the growth of enterprise except as it is able to pass on such new technology under a licensing program. There is some uneasiness in industry that government patents might become involved with antitrust policy in a way that has not thoroughly been thought through. Congressman Daddario has some important things to say on these policy issues in his chapter.

Corwin Edwards and others have pointed out that there is no further gain in economies of scale in a multi-plant operation beyond the spreading of central staff services over a greater volume of sales. The factor which these writers may be ignoring is the need to hedge the risks of market obsolescence. This is a factor often stressed in the search for suitable mergers. Companies are, in effect, seeking to broaden their technological base in the hope that they will always have an adequate number of innovations coming along in one field or another. The thrust toward the conglomerate firm is directed more toward reduction in risk than at an increase in efficiency. Each merger proposal must be looked at on its merits. Effective competition may be increased by a merger. For example, if companies B and C have a greatly increased chance for survival as a result of being merged, they may now constitute an effective counter weight to the leader, Company A. It is just possible that a similar conclusion may have been reached in the Lever Brothers case mentioned earlier. In dropping the action the government may have concluded that Lever Brothers with "All" might give Procter & Gamble more vigorous competition than Lever Brothers and Monsanto operating separately.

The characteristic antitrust problems arising in an industry are certainly related to technological advances but it is not a simple relationship which can be handled by per se rules. For example, a pool controlling patents on productive machinery is related to the classical conception of monopoly as control over supply. Patents pertaining to end products suggest the application of the concept of market power as defined by Dr. Kaysen.

In conclusion, three alternative policy positions are visualized regarding innovation and government control. The first of these, associated with the name of Joseph Schumpeter, took a somewhat fatalistic view toward the future of capitalism. The process of creative destruction would continue until capitalism had turned itself into another form of society. He suggested that these changes represent an inevitable trend and that there is little that can be done to stop it. Under this view we might fight a delaying action but never succeed in reversing the trend.

A second approach would be to try to maintain a free competitive economy relying mainly on punitive action. The government acts as a policeman and endeavors to maintain competition by proceeding against alleged monopolists. In addition to outright collusion for fixing prices or otherwise restraining trade, other actions are held to be unlawful because of the probability that they would promote monopoly. Various tests have been devised for the existence of monopoly or a tendency toward monopoly. Nearly all large companies bear some of the earmarks of monopoly and each of the giant corporations has been prosecuted time after time. All that is needed is some overt step which can be viewed as an infraction of the anti-trust laws. Doubtless these laws have had a moderating effect, but their impact on one business or another represents something less than even-handed justice.

The third view would endeavor to maintain competition largely through encouraging the entry and survival of new business. Government would be seen as a sort of market gardener selecting viable strains and making judicious use of fertilizers and irrigation. We are learning something about the ecology of business firms through technical aid programs in other countries, but it is time that we applied some of this new knowledge at home. It is certainly more difficult to develop an effective program for creating competitors than it is to persist in the present limited effort to regulate monopoly, but it might also be more rewarding.

There has been increasing attention to the problem of small

business in recent years. Every small business which succeeds contributes to making the economy more competitive. The Department of Agriculture has a vast organization to aid a class of enterprisers known as farmers, but the farmer is not typically small business any longer. As compared with the large commercial farm which can hire its own staff of specialists, there are many small businesses of the non-farm type which have greater need for expert advice and other services. The type of organization needed was described in a Converse Award lecture in 1953.

With respect to patents, Professor David Smith has correctly called attention to one of the hazards of the small business. That is becoming preoccupied with its patent position to the extent that it neglects to take the necessary steps to build its market position. If adequate means were found to provide business counsel to small business, the consultant might truthfully stress the abundance and availability of technology in many fields. That is the significance of the earlier analysis of patents in force and patents expired, pointing up the free availability of many fundamental technical ideas. Also to be watched is the government program for trying to promote widespread use under license of technical ideas generated in such areas as the space program.

Many of our ancestors lived on a geographical frontier. The importance of extending all proper aid to small firms operating on technological frontiers is coming to be recognized. Some of the projects in the Appalachia program hold the exciting prospect of rehabilitating some of those who live on this abandoned geographical frontier by a better planned and coordinated attack on certain sectors of the technological frontier.

Speaking from a background in business and engineering, Smith evaluates the role of patents today. He notes that technological change has had a major part in the extraordinary growth of "applied science" type industries in the past few decades. During this period, however, patents have declined in importance. He suggests that patents are still useful for nascent industries but that for major, large-scale programs, government support of research and development has superseded patents as the incentive for innovation.

DAVID B. SMITH is a professor in the Moore School of Electrical Engineering at the University of Pennsylvania. He graduated from the Hill School in 1929. He received his B.S. degree in Electrical Engineering in 1933 and his M.S. degree in 1934, both from the Massachusetts Institute of Technology.

Before coming to the University in 1964 he had spent his entire professional career with the Philco Corporation, becoming Director of Research and Development in 1940 and a vice president of the company in 1945.

CHAPTER 13

TECHNOLOGICAL INNOVATION
AND PATENTS

David Smith

In some remarks Dr. Louis Schwartz raised serious questions as to the current value to society of the Patent System. Before condemning the patent systems we would do well to determine not only what one expects of it and how well it is accomplishing its purpose—but in addition the influence of other new environmental factors which also bear on the same subject.

There would be little disagreement with the statement that the last quarter century has witnessed a major evolution in American industry and the marked increase in emphasis upon technological innovation as a driving force in this change.

There is a close parallel between the Toynbeeian "challenge and response" reactions of civilizations and those of industries. Industry does respond strongly to the challenges imposed by rapidly evolving science and technology. Particularly the "applied sciences" industries such as electronics and aerospace which account for the lion's share of R and D have in this period moved from the single-minded growth of youth and adolescence to the more diverse expansion of adulthood; from their initial preoccupation with products to their present preoccupation with large scale systems evolving from these products.

In this situation then it is essential to concentrate our attention on the dynamics of the company or industry; to establish its position in its life cycle, and to explore not only the current situation but also the events leading up to it and the probable consequences of current conditions.

245

In this dynamic model of the company reacting with its external environment, it is useful to categorize those factors that have a direct and immediate effect upon the profitability of the company; those that affect the rate of growth or decline of the company and still others that affect the rate of change of the growth rate. Each of those categories has a quite different effect upon the company and each must be examined by different criteria. For example, the "here and now things," the ability of the company to produce goods or service economically and to market them successfully, directly affect the current profitability of the firm. The immediacy of changes in the effectiveness of either of these company functions has made them relatively easy to understand and to measure.

However, the research and development function and its twin, the marketing function of identifying needs, do not in themselves create a direct and measurable profit factor. Rather these two functions create only the opportunity for future growth. This opportunity must then be successfully followed through by a subsequent production and marketing action to produce the end result upon the company. A successful R and D project, for example, could provide a growth opportunity of considerable value to company A, which had all the resources (marketing, production, etc.) necessary successfully to exploit it but exactly the same program could be completely unsuccessful in the hands of company B that lacked one or more of these latter resources.

Then, there are the factors which influence the ability of a company to conduct technical development programs or market research programs and thus effect the rate of change of growth. These include the environmental factors. The patent laws, the antitrust laws, and various other governmental regulations, for example, provide an environment which affects the ability of a company to conduct its growth functions. The results of modifications of this environment are usually not immediately apparent but they are long lasting and over time will bring about major changes in industry. This is the subject which we should examine.

What then is this environment and how has it changed in recent years? Over the past decade, total U.S. research and development expenditures have grown from a little more than 4 billion dollars to 16 billion. Of this amount that part conducted by industry has grown from about 3½ billion to 11.6 billion; the balance is performed largely in government labs and the rest in universities, etc. The share of industry research supported by the government has grown from about 1.4 billion to 6.7 billion. In those industries which have had the greatest growth in R and D, government support now amounts to something on the order of three fourths of the total effort. This support is, of course, accompanied by a similar increase in government control of the direction and management of research affairs.

During the same period, the number of patents issued has increased only by a nominal amount, from which one may conclude that patents are no longer as important as they once were. The essential statutory provisions for patents may be regarded as a governmental management policy type decision intended to create an environment which will encourage research and development. It is clear that in the early days of the republic this purpose was accomplished very well. Today this influence is clearly waning. Other environmental factors also established by governmental policy decisions are surpassing it in importance.

In the industries[1] with which I am familiar (i.e., applied science) four characteristics stand out, which may explain some of this loss of influence.

(1) In the generation of new business based upon new inventions, patents still serve their historical purpose of encouraging the inventor by giving him the opportunity to get started without interference from competition during the fledgling stage of his enterprise. In the electronics industry for example, there are many small companies successfully manufacturing new products based upon inventions and discoveries which represent significant scientific achievements. To a very considerable extent, the electronics industry in particular has grown in the past because of the availability of these inventions.

(2) It is characteristic of science and particularly technology that it grows upon itself. Each new advance adds to the total of technology which thus grows exponentially. The rapid increase in the capabilities of technology has in turn made it possible for scientists and engineers to become involved with increasingly complex problems and systems. This, in turn, has brought about the development of the

---

[1] One should distinguish between industries such as electronics and aerospace in which R and D is essentially socialized and industries such as petroleum, chemicals, and drugs in which it is not and R and D is largely supported by private profit. The following comments apply only to the former.

large, organized research and development of the large, organized research and development team approach to the solution of human needs and a moving away from the individual inventor approach. The Patent law, however, was specifically designed to reward the individual inventor and is not well adapted to the team concept. The individual inventor is finding it increasingly difficult to compete with teams of organized and highly trained professionals and in many cases the research facilities required are well beyond the capabilities of any but the largest companies.

(3) As industry and technology has grown, companies have grown with it. This has led naturally to the massing of patents in the hands of large companies and an extension of the patent monopoly beyond its initial intent. This, in turn, has led to the inevitable re-examination of the antitrust laws as applied to patent policies of large companies and the development of legal philosophies which considerably re-strain the uses to which patents may be put when they have passed from the hands of their inventor; and the evolution of antitrust restrictions upon the massing and package licensing of patents. It is also now generally true that a company which wishes to assert a large group of patents against a competitor can anticipate an antitrust type of counter-response which limits the value of patents in the hands of the larger and more mature organizations.

(4) In exchange for its support of R and D done for it by industry the government normally requires some form of license (i.e., freedom to make, have made, and sometimes control) for its purposes on inventions relating to this work. This, of course, reduces the value of such patents to the industrial concern doing the work and in turn their interest in obtaining patents. It is by no means clear that the government per se has the same interest in obtaining patents that a profit-motivated company has. This is not to say that government support of R and D in industry is not desirable but rather that it has superseded the patent as a more direct way of obtaining the desired innovation. Thus it is national policy to encourage innovation. The Patent system does so by providing an indirect opportunity for reward to the creative individual free to choose his own technical field. Direct government payment for work in specific R and D areas, however, is clearly a far more powerful means of obtaining new technology in those fields the government decides to support. It is not likely for example, that the most favorable form of patent policy

that could be devised would have brought about the industrial development of atomic energy, but direct government subsidy of R and D by industry in this field has successfully done so. However, this also reacts to the disadvantage of our inventor-entrepreneur of (1) above who generally cannot—on his own funds and future hopes—compete with a government subsidized competitor in the same field.

Professor Alderson, in his preceding paper, has suggested that the attitude of a company and the value of patents to it depends upon whether the company is a supplier or end-product manufacturer. I would like to suggest that a better distinction might be whether or not the industry is in its youth phase, or is a mature industry. There seems to be no question but that the patent system does create an environment which is helpful in initiating business enterprises based upon distinctly new products as opposed to improvements in old products. However, in a more mature industry, the basic inventions have been made and current inventions are in the nature of improvements which must displace an existing way of doing business to be successful. Here then other factors become important. Clearly the end-product manufacturer does wish to differentiate his product from that of his competitors but he must also do this in a way which permits him to be competitive in terms of price and other value factors. It is a tribute to American industry that generally the customer has considerable confidence in the technical performance of its products. Customers take for granted that an automobile or a refrigerator or a television set will perform in a reliable and technically satisfactory manner. They are not particularly interested in what is under the hood. If, however, the manufacturer of such a product wishes to introduce a patentable new innovation such as, for example, a new vacuum tube or a new compressor, and this device is patentably different; then, if he wishes to keep it to himself, he must face the problem of economy of scale and the added cost of production of the non-standard item. One then has to examine the question of the improvement in saleability of one's product in the market taking into account the additional performance which may be obtained against the increase in cost due to the lack of standardization. Many new innovations fail to meet this test.

The supplier to the end-product manufacturer faces a somewhat similar situation. The end-product manufacturer's purchasing agent will make a value analysis of new products offered to him. In this evaluation, price, availability of the product, performance, and so forth are weighed in terms of their effect upon the end-product itself. This is not to say that the supplier does not gain from bringing a patented product to the end-product manufacturer provided he can successfully compete in the areas of cost, availability, and performance. The difficulty that often obtains is that the supplier does not make the proper management decision to concentrate upon those areas (i.e., cost, availability, performance) which directly affect saleability and to consider his patent position as a useful but not essential business aid. Certainly in the broad complex of mass-production, mature industries, there are many companies (suppliers as well as end product manufacturers) who have not succeeded because of the preoccupation with designing their products from the point of view of obtaining patents instead of meeting their customers real needs. A not infrequent comment of chief engineers to their president is the question; "Do you want me to get you patents or successful products?" It is much more difficult to do both.

The above discussion leads to the following conclusions: In the last quarter century there has been an extraordinary growth of "applied science" type industries. Technological innovation, which the Patent System is intended to encourage, has certainly played a major role in this growth. During this same period, however, patents have declined in importance. The influence of the Patent System on industry is clearly less now than it was in the earlier days of the industrial revolution.

Patents do encourage innovation of new devices which can generate new industries and thus serve a useful purpose especially with respect to significant new inventions. This is particularly true for the individual inventor and small business. However, we are now in a state of technology where we can also think of major new programs of tremendous scale. Such advances require large organized teams of engineers and scientists. In such cases direct government support of R and D has superseded patents as the incentive for innovation and certainly is far more effective. In this area of socialized technology the patent system is somewhat of an anachronism. Considerable thought should be given to the role of patents—if any—in this area of our economy.

In the more mature industries particularly those of a mass production nature, patents have accomplished their primary role and should play only a secondary part. A more precise definition of the anti-trust laws as applied to patents—particularly the massing of patents and the licensing (or failure to license) large collections of patents would be helpful.

Finally, discontent with patents could be reduced if their role were more clearly understood. Patents should not be expected to perform the same function in mature industries that they do in nascent ones; nor the same role in industries with socialized R and D as against those in which R and D is supported out of profits. Nor should we charge the patent system with antitrust problems brought about at least in part by the growth of the economy,—nor fail to correct those problems.

Technological innovation is essential for our economy. The patent system is not performing its function of encouraging innovation as well as it should and other influences may be superseding it in some areas. What is needed is a better understanding of the role of Science and Technology in our economy including the role the government is to play and a revision of the patent laws in the light of this understanding.